C000015479

Contents

Preface

Preface

The Toolbox Guide is intended to provide guidance to
electrical contractors on the requirements of *BS 7671 :
2008* Requirements for Electrical Installations (IEE Wiring
Regulations Seventeenth Edition)

BS 7671 : 2008 Requirements for Electrical Installations was
issued on 1st January 2008 and is intended to come into
effect on 1st July 2008. *BS 7671 : 2008* includes changes
necessary to maintain technical alignment with CENELEC
harmonisation documents. Where appropriate the main
changes are identified within this guide.

The guide is intended to complement other authoritative
guidance published by NICEIC and the Institution of
Electrical Engineers.

It is intended as a handy toolbox guide to simple, common
types of installation. It is not intended to be a substitute for
BS 7671 which should be consulted for conditions outside
the scope of this guide or in cases of doubt. Electricians
should always consult *BS 7671* to satisfy themselves that
the requirements have been met.

The guide is not intended to instruct untrained and
inexperienced persons to undertake electrical installation
work. It assumes persons proposing to undertake such
work have already acquired the necessary knowledge,
understanding and skill, and are properly equipped to
undertake such work without putting themselves or others
at risk.

Introduction

Introduction

The introduction of the *BS 7671 : 2008* Requirements for Electrical Installations (IEE Wiring Regulations 17th Edition) has naturally brought about changes from the 16th Edition. The aim of this guide is to help familiarisation with the new requirements whilst not concentrating solely on the changes.

The format of the guide generally follows that of *BS 7671* to help familiarisation and any cross-referencing which will be required for a more detailed study of the standard.

The Pre-work survey section provides information and a reminder that this element is vital to the planning of both new installations and the addition or alteration to existing installations. At the end of the section is a handy checklist to serve as a reminder of typical aspects which form part of the survey.

Within each section there are reminders of common departures from *BS 7671* that are sometimes found in electrical installations. These are highlighted for easy reference and will help avoid similar departures in the future.

As the guide is intended as a handy toolbox guide a more detailed section on Inspecting and Testing has been included which provides a practical approach and guidance on the correct procedures.

Within the Appendices example calculations are provided to encourage familiarisation with the procedure, for the correct selection of the cross-sectional area of conductors.

Pre-work survey

The aim of this section is to encourage a thorough survey of the existing installation, prior to any additions and/or alterations. The addition or alteration may only be of a minor nature, (such as the addition of a lighting point, or socket-outlet) or may be major (such as the introduction of new final circuits).

Whether the addition or alteration is of a minor or major nature, the relevant requirements of *BS7671* have to be met such that both the addition or alteration is safe, and the safety of the existing installation is not impaired.

The checklist provided at the end of this section will help identify the more common items that need to be checked.

1.0 Additions and alterations

The following should be considered before carrying out an addition or alteration:

- assessment of the existing installation to establish the rating and condition of the existing equipment, including the distributor's, will be adequate for the altered circumstances.
- whether the parts of the existing installation which the addition or alteration will rely upon for safety, are both present and suitable for the altered circumstances, and will continue to be so.
- whether any upgrading is required to parts of the installation as a result of the above assessment, in order to accommodate the addition or alteration.

- that the design and construction of the addition or alteration shall be in accordance with *BS 7671*
- inspection and testing of any upgrading and of the addition or alteration, before being put into service, shall be carried out in accordance with Chapter 61 of *BS 7671*
- the certification of any upgrading and of the addition or alteration should be carried out in accordance with Chapter 63 of *BS 7671*

Regulation 131.8 states that no addition or alteration, temporary or permanent, shall be made to an existing installation unless it has been ascertained that the rating and condition of the existing installation, including that of the distributor, is adequate for the altered circumstances. It also states that the earthing and bonding arrangements, which any addition or alteration relies upon, shall be adequate.

Consideration of the supply Electrical system and earthing arrangement, number and type of live conductors, supply capacity, overcurrent protective device and the presence and adequacy of the earthing and bonding arrangements will be among the first considerations before any work is to be carried out.

In addition to this, before selection of a wiring system, it will be necessary to ensure that not only is the proposed new wiring system compatible with the existing, but also that it has been selected correctly in accordance with Part 5 of the regulations.

2.0 Existing earthing and bonding arrangements

As part of the general assessment of the installation, it will be necessary to determine which type of earthing system the installation is to use.

Pre-work survey

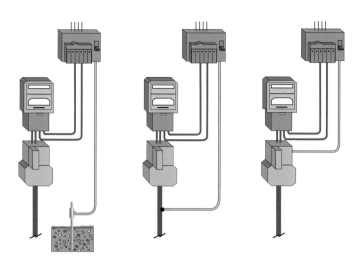

Fig 2.1 Drawings of TT, TN-S & TN-C-S arrangements

For a TN-S system, the neutral conductor and the protective conductor are separate conductors in the supply cable.

For a TN-C-S system the neutral and the protective conductor are combined within one conductor in the supply cable (a PEN conductor). This system is sometimes referred to as a PME supply.

For a TT system there is no protective conductor provided with the supply cable and the installation is earthed by means of an installation earth electrode.

Whichever type of earthing system is employed, it will be necessary to check that the earthing conductor is present, is of the correct cross-sectional area and is correctly installed and connected. A thorough investigation must be carried out in order to determine whether what appears to be an existing earthing facility is actually an effective means of earthing.

For a new TT system, it will be necessary to install an installation earth electrode and associated earthing conductor.

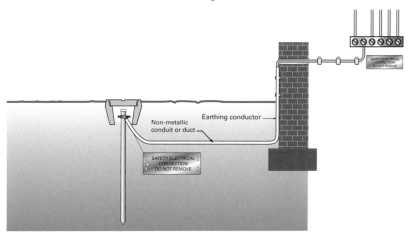

Fig 2.2 Earth electrode with earthing conductor connected

A test should be carried out to determine the prospective fault current (I_{pf}) and the external earth loop impedance (Z_e) at the origin of the supply. The circuit protective device that protects the circuit that is to be added to or altered, must be capable of withstanding the fault current available. The measurement of the external earth fault loop impedance will not only check that the supply has an earthing facility, but will also provide a value to use for calculation of the circuit earth fault loop impedance (Z_s).

Often overlooked is Regulation 411.3.1.2 which states the requirement to provide main protective bonding conductors, connecting the main earthing terminal (MET) to any extraneous-conductive-parts. These may be gas and/or water installation pipes, structural steelwork, lightning protection systems, and any other extraneous-conductive-part that enters the building.

Published by NICEIC. © Electrical Safety Council (Jan 2008)

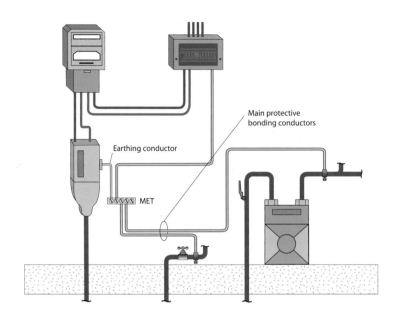

Fig 2.3 Main protective bonding requirements

Practically this requires that when carrying out an addition or alteration to the electrical installation, if main protective bonding conductors are required due to the presence of extraneous-conductive-parts, but are not currently installed, then they must be installed as part of the addition or alteration.

Furthermore, they must be installed correctly and be of the correct cross-sectional area. It may be necessary to replace existing conductors due to incorrect sizing, conductors that are in poor condition or not proved to be continuous.

Sizing of these conductors must be accordance with Regulation 544.1.1 and installed in accordance with Regulation 544.1.2.

If the addition or alteration is within a special location or part of an installation classified as a special location, then additional requirements may be necessary in accordance with Part 7.

Additions or alterations to the installation in a room containing a bath or shower would require an assessment of any existing supplementary bonding, which if required, connects the exposed-conductive-parts to the extraneous-conductive-parts.

Common departures
1. Adequacy of earthing and bonding has not been fully assessed prior to an alteration or addition.
2. Main protective bonding conductors are not present or are undersized.
3. Supplementary bonding conductors are of insufficient cross-sectional area.
4. Absence of a terminated circuit protective conductor at every accessory.

3.0 Upgrading of an existing installation

After an assessment of the existing installation has been carried out and it is not adequate to support the proposed addition or alteration safely, then either:

- the work must not proceed and the client advised immediately, preferably in writing.

- the necessary upgrading work is recommended to the client and with consent, is carried out prior to the addition or alteration being put into service.

Compatability

To ensure compatibility with the rest of the installation, every item of equipment should be selected so that it will neither cause harmful effects to other equipment nor impair the supply during normal service, including switching operations.

Chapter 33 provides examples of characteristics that may have harmful effects upon other equipment or services and include for example:

- Unbalanced loads
- Rapidly fluctuating loads
- Starting currents
- Harmonic currents
- Leakage currents
- Excessive protective conductor current

Maintainability

Chapter 34 requires that an assessment should be made of the frequency and quality of the maintenance that the installation is reasonably expected to receive, during its intended life. This may involve consultation with the person responsible for the operation and/or maintenance.

Practical examples of how this requirement is met would be to ensure that:

- Any periodic inspection and testing, maintenance and necessary repairs can be carried out readily and safely during the intended life of the installation

- The protective measures for safety shall remain effective for the intended life of the installation

- The reliability of any equipment for proper functioning is appropriate to the intended life of the installation

4.0 Assessment of load

If the addition or alteration demands an additional load on the existing installation, then an assessment of both the additional load and that of the existing load will have to be carried out. Can the supply arrangement and the service cut-out device carry the additional load?

If a new circuit is to be utilized, then in order to meet the requirements of Regulation 433.1.1, it will be necessary to provide an additional circuit protective device, and therefore the existing consumer unit will have to allow the provision of the new circuit by means of a spare way.

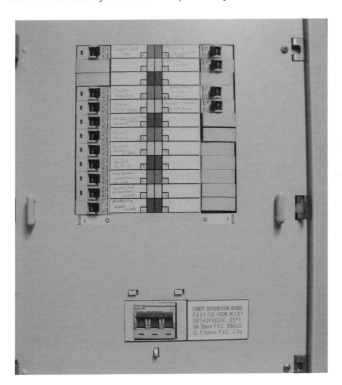

Fig 2.4 Distribution board with spare ways

5.0 Selection of wiring system

The wiring system selected should be suitable for the intended purpose and therefore appropriate to any external influences that the installation may be expected to experience. This applies not only to the type of cables used but to their connections, any jointing or terminations and supports and suspensions of the wiring system.

Chapter 52 of *BS 7671* provides the requirements for the selection and erection of wiring systems. As part of the pre-work survey it will be necessary to take into account the type of installation, the installed conditions, and the intended use of the existing installation that additions or alterations apply to.

Common departures
1. Wiring system is not suitable for the external influences.
2. Wiring system not adequately supported.
3. Terminations are not enclosed in a suitable enclosure.
4. Cables in walls not installed in prescribed zones where required and/or do not have RCD protection where required.
5. Consideration of eddy currents not been given to the installation of single-core cables.

6.0 Circuit design

If the work involved incorporates new wiring then this is required to meet the relevant requirements of *BS 7671*. The design current of the new or altered circuit will have to be considered when selecting the rating of the circuit protective device, or checking that any existing device is suitable.

The installed conditions of any new wiring shall be considered in terms of:

• whether the cables are grouped with other cables

- the ambient temperature of the installed cables

- whether the cables are in contact with any thermal insulation

- whether the circuit protective device is a semi-enclosed fuse *(BS 3036)*

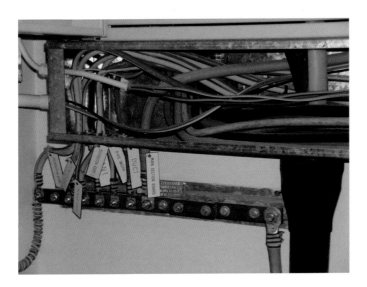

Fig 2.5 Cables enclosed within trunking

If any of the above are relevant this may effect the current-carrying capacity of the proposed wiring and the appropriate calculations should be carried out.

Example cable calculations are provided in the appendix of this guide.

Common departures
1. Excessive Earth Fault Loop Impedance, disconnection times exceeded.
2. Cables inadequately protected against impact.
3. Circuits supplying current-using equipment in a location containing a bath or shower not protected by an RCD with a value not exceeding 30 mA

7.0 Pre-work Survey Checklist

The following checklist provides a list of items to be verified as part of the pre-work survey prior to any addition or alteration being carried out. The list is not exhaustive and it may be necessary to carry out further checks relevant to the existing installation.

1. Identify the type or earthing arrangement that is provided. ☐

2. Will the supply arrangement, including cut-out fuse, take the additional load? ☐

3. Is the earthing conductor present, effective, correctly sized and installed? ☐

4. Are there any main protective bonding conductors connected to extraneous parts, water, gas, oil, structural steel, etc? ☐

5. Is supplementary bonding required in the bathroom? ☐

6. Does the existing consumer unit have spare capacity to take the additional circuit(s)? ☐

7. Is there a need to provide an RCD for fault protection – TT system? ☐

8. What kind of protective device is to be used for the new circuit(s)? ☐

9. What will be the rating of the protective device installed and has it been selected taking into consideration the design current of the circuit? ☐

10. Is there a need to provide an RCD to protect socket-outlets? ☐

11. What cable type, size and method of installation should be used? ☐

12. What labels are required for the installation? ☐

13. Have sample checks for continuity of protective conductors, polarity, insulation resistance and earth fault loop impedance been carried out on circuits that are to be added to or altered? ☐

14. Are there any notable defects, (such as unsatisfactory wiring), in the installation? ☐

If a consumer unit change is being considered without the rewiring of part or whole of the connected final circuits, then the Electricity Safety Council best practice guide offers guidance on how this may be carried out.

Part 3
Assessment of General Characteristics

Part 3 of *BS 7671* comprises only a short section of the standard, but is however very important. The designer of an electrical installation is required to make the necessary assessments of the general characteristics of the installation in terms of the design, construction and maintenance.

The Chapters within Part 3 provide the requirements for the assessment of:

31. Purpose for which the installation is intended, its general structure and its supplies.
32. The external influences to which it is to be exposed
33. The compatibility of its equipment
34. Its maintainability
35. Recognised safety services
36. Assessment of continuity of service

3.1   Purpose, supplies and structure (Chapter 31)

Chapter 31 requires that assessment be made of the maximum demand, taking into account any diversity that may be applicable.

The maximum demand is the maximum anticipated load of the installation, plus an additional allowance for any increase in load in the future. If this is not assessed properly then the installation, or part of it, may suffer from becoming overloaded.

The estimation of maximum demand is sometimes difficult to carry out accurately and historic data and experience of circuit and equipment usage will enable a more accurate assessment of the demand.

If diversity is not taken into account, then supplies and distribution may be larger than necessary, resulting in an uneconomic provision.

Maximum demand and diversity are related by the following equation:

Maximum demand = Connected load x Diversity factor

The diversity factor makes allowance that not all the connected load will be used at the same time. Therefore analysis of the connected load, how and when it will be used, is required to determine whether diversity can be applied.

Examples of factors that should be considered;

- whether the loads will be used at the same time
- how long the loads are expected to be used for
- the mechanical loading of any motors or services' plant
- seasonal requirements in terms of heating, cooling and lighting
- specific requirements to the installation, for example use of hotel bedrooms, classrooms and workshops. Will all rooms be occupied and demanding load? If so how much?

Common departures
1. Account has not been taken of the operation or failure of a single protective device.
2. A final circuit has not been connected to a separate way in the distribution board.

3.2 Supplies

Regulation 313.1 requires the designer of an installation to assess the characteristics of the supply or supplies, prior to any new work or any additions and alterations.

The earthing system adopted by the designer will generally be determined by the earthing system of the electricity supply. Typical arrangements will be TN-S, TN-C-S (PME) or TT.

BS 7671 requires the designer to determine the nature of the supply. This information will normally be provided by the Distributor for supplies provided by them, but can be determined by calculation, enquiry or inspection (measurement) and will include;

- nominal voltage
- nature of the current – normally 400 V and/or 230 V (a.c.)
- frequency – normally 50 Hz
- prospective short circuit current at the origin
- earth fault loop impedance Z_e, of the part of the system external to the installation – more frequently referred to as the external loop impedance
- suitability for the requirements of the installation, including maximum demand
- type and rating of the overcurrent protective device acting at the origin of the installation

In addition to this, the number of live conductors will need to be determined when making an assessment of the general characteristics, as this information is required for completion of electrical installation certificates and periodic inspection reports.

Common departures

1. Characteristics of the supply have not been determined, V, Z_e, Ipf, Max demand and protective device at the origin.

3.3   Division of the installation

Regulation 314.1 requires that every installation be divided into circuits, as necessary to:

- avoid danger and minimise inconvenience in the event of a fault
- facilitate safe inspection, testing and maintenance
- take account of the danger that may arise from the failure of a single circuit such as a lighting circuit

- reduce the possibility of unwanted tripping of RCDs due to excessive protective conductor currents produced by equipment in normal operation
- reduce the effects of electromagnetic interferences (EMI)
- prevent the indirect energising of a circuit intended to be isolated

Practically this requires the designer to consider carefully the number of circuits within the intended installation, and their protective devices, to ensure that only the circuits where, faults occur, are disconnected.

Common departures
1. Installation has not been divided to minimise inconvenience for faults and facilitate inspection & testing.

3.4   External influences (Chapter 32)

The electrical installation which includes the wiring system and any items of equipment, shall be selected and installed taking into account the situation in which it is to be used and conditions likely to be encountered. **These are the external influences.**

3.1 Cables that have been eaten by mice

For more information on external influences refer to Part 5 selection and erection of equipment, or appropriate topics of the Technical Manual published by The Electrical Safety Council.

3.5 Compatibility (Chapter 33)

This chapter deals with compatibility within the installation of any equipment that may have harmful effects upon other items of electrical equipment. Chapter 33 lists some characteristics that may cause harmful effects, and include:

- transient overvoltages
- unbalanced loads
- starting currents
- harmonic currents
- earth leakage currents
- excessive protective conductor currents not due to a fault

Equipment that is subject to frequent load change, for example X-Ray machines, welding equipment and large motors, may cause interference in supplies to other equipment.

Examples of this interference include lamps flickering and small motors tripping out on their no-volt release as other equipment has caused a voltage drop in their supply. Consideration should therefore be given to the design of the installation if the characteristics of equipment intended to be installed is likely to cause these harmful effects.

3.6 Maintainability (Chapter 34)

This chapter, although brief, requires the designer to assess how the installation is to be maintained. It requires knowledge of the frequency and quality of maintenance that the installation can be expected to receive during its intended life. In order to assess this it will be necessary to consult the person or body responsible for the operation and/or maintenance.

The design and installation of the electrical installation should ensure that:

- any periodic inspection, maintenance and repairs can be readily and safely carried out
- the effectiveness of the protective measures for safety during the intended life shall not diminish
- the reliability for proper functioning of the installation is appropriate to the intended life

Assessment of General Characteristics

3.2 Electrician carrying out maintenance

Examples of the more obvious areas include the replacement of lamps, accessibility of switchgear, and the repair and maintenance of electrical equipment. Provision shall be made to facilitate these functions.

3.7 Safety services (Chapter 35)

As part of the assessment of general characteristics Chapter 35 deals with safety services.

Examples of safety services are:
- emergency escape lighting
- fire alarm systems
- installation of fire pumps
- rescue service lifts
- smoke and heat extraction equipment

Chapter 35 states that these safety services are frequently regulated by statutory authorities whose requirements have to be met.

They are also often the subject of separate British Standards, for example, *BS 5839* : Fire detection and fire alarm systems for buildings and *BS 5266* : Emergency lighting.

The following sources for safety services are recognised:

- storage batteries
- primary cells
- generator sets independent of the normal supply
- a separate feeder of the supply network effectively independent of the normal feeder

3.8 Continuity of service (Chapter 36)

A new chapter with the introduction of the 17th edition of the standard requires that an assessment should be made for each circuit of any need for the continuity of service considered necessary during the intended life of the installation. An example of this would be a life support system.

In carrying out this assessment, consideration should be given to:

- selection of the system earthing
- selection of the protective device in order to achieve discrimination
- number of circuits
- multiple power supplies
- use of monitoring devices

Part 4
Protection For Safety

Part 4 of *BS 7671* deals with protection for safety and is
split up into four chapters:

- Chapter 41 Protection against electric shock
- Chapter 42 Protection against thermal effects
- Chapter 43 Protection against overcurrent
- Chapter 44 Protection against voltage disturbances and
  electromagnetic disturbances

This is a very important part of the standard as it is concerned
with safety and how the design and installation must satisfy
the requirements to provide the protection for safety.

4.0   Protection against electric shock (Chapter 41)

In order to protect against electric shock the installation
should not have any accessible hazardous-live-parts.
Protection can be provided by means of insulation for
example, preventing contact with live parts. However the
installation may at some stage experience a fault and, even
under these conditions, shock protection must be provided.

Terms that were used in the 16th edition of *BS 7671* were
direct contact and indirect contact, which have been
replaced in the 17th edition by new terms.

- **Direct contact** has been replaced with **basic protection**
- **Indirect contact** has been replaced with **fault protection**

Chapter 41 specifies the essential requirements regarding
both basic and fault protection for persons and livestock. It
deals also with the application and co-ordination of these
requirements in relation to external influences.

4.0.1   Automatic disconnection of supply (411)

The protective measure automatic disconnection of supply
provides basic protection by basic insulation of live parts, or
by barriers and enclosures.

Automatic disconnection of supply provides fault protection by protective earthing, protective equipotential bonding and automatic disconnection of the supply in the case of a fault. This method of protection was referred to as EEBAD (protection by Earthed Equipotential Bonding and Automatic Disconnection of Supply) in the 16th edition of *BS 7671* and is now referred to as **ADS** (Automatic Disconnection of Supply).

Fault protection provided by PEBAD is achieved by connecting together extraneous-conductive-parts and exposed-conductive-parts.

Examples of exposed-conductive-parts:

- Metal case of an appliance
- Metal light fitting
- Metal frame of an electric motor

Protective earthing is provided where exposed-conductive-parts are connected to the protective earthing terminal by means of circuit protective conductors. A circuit protective conductor should be run to each point on the circuit and terminated properly.

Simultaneously accessible exposed-conductive-parts should be connected to the same earthing system individually, in groups or collectively.

Examples of extraneous-conductive-parts:

- Incoming metal gas installation pipe
- Incoming metal water installation pipe
- Structural steelwork

Protective equipotential bonding is provided where extraneous-conductive-parts are connected to the protective earthing terminal by means of main protective bonding conductors in accordance with Chapter 54.

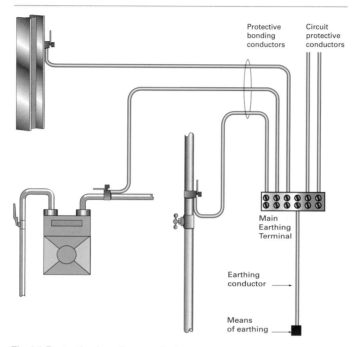

Fig 4.1 Protective bonding conductors

For automatic disconnection of supply to provide protection, it relies upon sufficient current to operate the protective device (fuse, circuit-breaker or RCD) in the event of an earth fault. The disconnection must also be achieved within a specified time.

In a TN sytem where a circuit is not covered by Regulation 411.3.2.2 a disconnection time not exceeding 5 seconds is permitted for a distribution circuit or a final circuit exceeding 32 A.

In a TT system where a circuit is not covered by Regulation 411.3.2.2 a disconnection time not exceeding 1 second is permitted for a distribution circuit or a final circuit exceeding 32 A.

Where the disconnection times according to Regulation 411.3.2.1 cannot be achieved supplementary equipotential bonding should be provided in accordance with Regulation 415.2.

The maximum disconnection times are shown below, from Regulation 411.3.2.2

Table 41.1 Maximum disconnection times (Regulation 411.3.2.2)

System	$50V < U_0 \le 120V$ seconds		$120V < U_0 \le 230V$ seconds		$230V < U_0 \le 400V$ seconds		$U_0 > 400V$ seconds	
	a.c	d.c	a.c	d.c	a.c	d.c	a.c	d.c
TN	0.8	Note 1	0.4	5	0.2	0.4	0.1	0.1
TT	0.3	Note 1	0.2	0.4	0.07	0.2	0.04	0.1

U_0 is the nominal a.c. rms or d.c. line voltage to Earth.

Note 1: Disconnection is not required for protection against electric shock but may be required for other reasons, such as protection against thermal effects.

Note 2: Where compliance with this regulation is provided by an RCD, the disconnection times in accordance with Table 41.1 relate to prospective residual fault currents significantly higher than the rated residual operating current of the RCD (typically $2 I_{\Delta n}$).

In practice, compliance with the requirements of maximum disconnection times are met if the circuit meets maximum earth fault loop impedance values for the chosen circuit protective device. (Tables 41.2, 41.3, 41.4 and 41.5)

The circuit designer will ensure any proposed circuit arrangement meets these requirements, as circuit length, cross-sectional area of conductors and the external loop impedance of the supply all affect the earth fault loop impedance path.

Socket-outlets - Additional protection by RCD

Socket-outlets with a rated current up to 20A, for general use by ordinary persons, are now required to have additional protection by an RCD with an $I_{\Delta n}$ not exceeding 30mA.

This requirement also applies to mobile equipment with a current-rating not exceeding 32A for use outdoors.

The above RCD protection for socket-outlets may be omitted where:

- They are under the supervision of a skilled or instructed person (e.g. some commercial/industrial locations)
- A socket-outlet is labelled for use with a specific item of equipment e.g. a fridge.

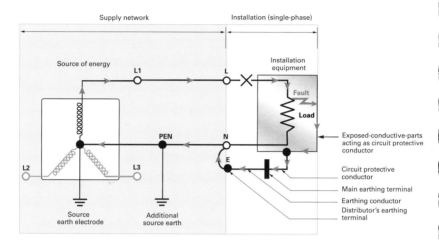

Denotes path of fault current

X   Denotes circuit-protective device (overcurrent)

Fig 4.2 TN-C-S earth fault loop (showing earth fault path)

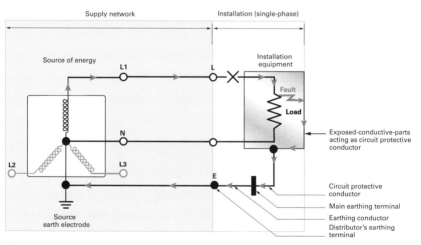

Denotes path of fault current

X   Denotes circuit-protective device (overcurrent)

Fig 4.3 TN-S earth fault loop (showing earth fault path)

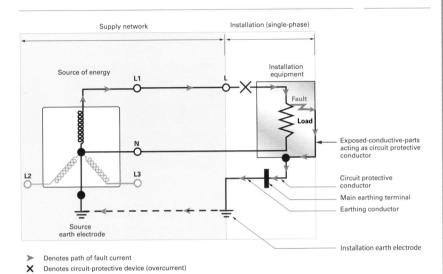

Supply network · Installation (single-phase)

> Denotes path of fault current
✗ Denotes circuit-protective device (overcurrent)

Fig 4.4 TT system - earth fault loop impedance path

Sample calculations to meet earth fault loop impedance requirements are provided in the appendices.

4.0.2 Double or reinforced insulation (412)

The protective measure double or reinforced insulation relies on the use of equipment having no exposed metal parts on which a dangerous voltage could appear, in the event of a failure of the basic insulation of a live part. Double insulation applies to items such as luminaires, appliances and some assemblies of switchgear and control gear.

Usually there is another protective measure in place within the installation, but if double or reinforced insulation is the sole protective measure, it must only be used under effective supervision in normal use, ensuring no change could be made that would impair the effectiveness of the protective measure.

Basic and fault protection can be provided in the case of double or reinforced insulation. With double insulation the basic protection is provided by the basic insulation and fault protection provided by the supplementary insulation.

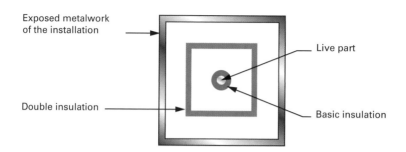

Exposed metalwork
of the installation

Live part

Double insulation

Basic insulation

Fig 4.5 Diagram of double insulation

Reinforced insulation provides both basic and fault protection.

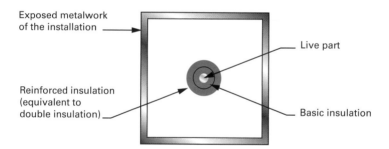

Exposed metalwork
of the installation

Live part

Reinforced insulation
(equivalent to
double insulation)

Basic insulation

Fig 4.6 Reinforced insulation

Electrical equipment that has been type-tested to Class II,
is equipment having either double or reinforced insulation
and, has the following identification symbol.

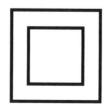

Fig 4.7 Class II symbol

If equipment does not carry this symbol it cannot be assumed that it is Class II simply because it may have an insulated case or enclosure.

A circuit supplying one or more items of Class II equipment should have a circuit protective conductor run to and properly terminated at each point and at each accessory. This provision takes into account that the Class II equipment could be replaced at some stage by items of Class I equipment.

Cables having a non-metallic sheath or non-metallic enclosures are considered to meet the requirements of *BS 7671* for protection by use of Class II equipment or equivalent insulation. The requirements of Chapter 52 must be met when installing such wiring systems.

Types of cable having a non-metallic sheath include:

- PVC/PVC Insulated and sheathed cables to *BS 6004*

Examples of non-metallic enclosures include:

- Plastic conduit systems
- Plastic trunking

4.0.3 Electrical separation (413)

Electrical separation is a protective measure in which:

- basic protection is provided by basic insulation of live parts or by barriers or enclosures
- fault protection is provided by simple separation of the separated circuit from other circuits and from earth

Normally this is achieved by utilising an isolating transformer; a common example is a shaver supply unit complying with *BS EN 61558-2-5*.

This is covered under Section 413 which limits the use under this protective measure to the supply of one item of current-using equipment supplied from one unearthed source with simple separation.

Basic protection is provided by basic insulation, or by barriers or enclosures, or by double or reinforced insulation.

Requirements for fault protection are:

- the separated circuit being supplied through a source with at least simple separation, and not exceeding 500 V
- live parts of the separated circuit should not be connected at any point to another circuit or to Earth or to a protective conductor
- flexible cables should be visible throughout any part of their length liable to mechanical damage
- for separated circuits, the use of a separate wiring system is recommended. If run with other circuits the requirements of Regulation 413.3.5 shall be met
- no conductive part of the separated circuit shall be connected to the protective conductor or exposed-conductive-parts of other circuits, or to Earth

Where more than one item is supplied from a single source, as may be the case in a workshop or laboratory where a separated source supplies a series of socket-outlets, then those installations should meet the requirements of Section 518.

4.0.4 Extra-low voltage provided by SELV and PELV (414)

Protection by extra-low voltage is a protective measure which consists of either of two different extra-low voltage systems:

- SELV – Separated extra-low voltage
- PELV – Protected extra-low voltage

Protection by extra-low voltage provided by SELV or PELV requires:

- limitation of the voltage in the system to the upper limit of voltage Band I, 50 V a.c. or 120 V d.c, and
- protective separation of the SELV or PELV system from all other circuits other than SELV and PELV circuits, and basic insulation between the SELV and PELV system and other SELV and PELV sytems, and
- for SELV system only, basic insulation between the SELV system and Earth.

SELV

A SELV system is

'An extra-low voltage system which is electrically separated from Earth and from other systems in such a way that a single fault cannot give rise to the risk of an electric shock'

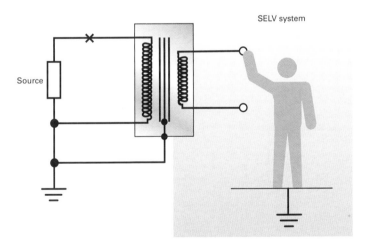

Fig 4.8 A SELV system illustrating shock protection

In some situations such as special locations or installations (Part 7 of *BS 7671*) the upper limit of voltage Band I may have to be reduced.

Sources of SELV and PELV

The most common source of SELV is the safety isolating transformer conforming to *BS EN 61558-2-6.*

A motor-generator can be used as a SELV source provided that it meets the same requirements for voltage and electrical separation as the safety isolating transformer.

Other sources for the provision of SELV include an electrochemical source, e.g. a battery or a diesel-driven generator, providing it is independent of a higher voltage circuit.

PELV

A PELV system is,

'An extra-low voltage system which is not electrically separated from Earth, but which otherwise satisfies all the requirements for SELV'

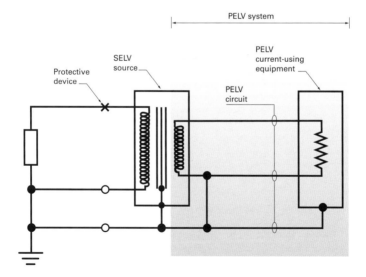

Fig 4.9 A PELV system

Basic and fault protection for SELV and PELV

Basic and fault protection is provided when:

- the nominal voltage cannot exceed 50 V a.c. and 120 V ripple-free d.c. and
- the supply is from one of the sources listed in Regulation 414.3 and
- the conditions of Regulation Group 414.4 are fulfilled.

Basic protection by means of insulation and/or barriers or enclosures may also be required where the nominal voltage exceeds 25 V a.c. or 60 V d.c. or if the equipment is subjected to certain external influences, e.g. immersion.

It is important that the integrity of the protection provided by the SELV or PELV source is not reduced by the detrimental effects of other circuits. Where the SELV or PELV source supplies a single piece of equipment this is unlikely to be the case, but the requirements of Regulations 414.4.1 and 414.4.2 need to be met to ensure that the protective measure is maintained.

Where SELV or PELV socket-outlets or luminaire supporting couplers are installed they should not be dimensionally compatible with those used for any other system in use in the same premises.

Plugs and socket-outlets in a SELV system must not have a protective conductor contact.

4.0.5 Additional protection (415)

The use of an RCD is recognised as additional protection under certain circumstances, such as where there may be a concern about the failure of basic protection and /or fault protection. Carelessness by users of the installation or electrical equipment may also necessitate the provision of additional protection by means of an RCD. The RCD used in such circumstances should have a rated residual operating current not exceeding 30 mA and an operating time not exceeding 40 ms at a residual current of 5 $I_{\Delta n}$.

Supplementary equipotential bonding may also be required as an addition to fault protection. This may involve the entire installation, part of the installation, an item of equipment or a location, and should include all simultaneously accesible exposed-conductive-parts of fixed equipment and extraneous-conductive-parts.

4.0.6   Provision for Basic Protection (416)

The definition of basic protection is "protection against electric shock under fault-free conditions"

Protection must therefore be provided to prevent persons or livestock from making contact with live parts. This may be achieved by insulating live parts or by providing a barrier or enclosure which prevents access to the live parts.

An electric shock normally occurs by either contact with a live part whilst in contact with Earth, (between line and Earth) or by contact with live conductors which are at different potentials (between line and neutral, or different lines of a three-phase installation).

Regulation 410.3.2 states the requirements for a protective measure and that it should consist of:

- an appropriate combination of a provision for basic protection *and*
- an independent provision for fault protection, *or*
- an enhanced protective provision which provides both basic and fault protection.

Additional protection may be required under certain conditions of external influences or certain special locations.

In each part of the electrical installation one or more protective measures should be applied. The following protective measures generally are permitted:

- automatic disconnection of the supply
- double or reinforced insulation
- electrical separation for the supply to one item of current-using equipment
- extra-low voltage (SELV and PELV)

Automatic disconnection of supply

Automatic disconnection of a supply is a protective measure in which basic protection is provided, by basic insulation and by barriers and enclosures, **and in addition** to this, fault protection is provided by protective equipotential bonding and automatic disconnection in the event of a fault.

All electrical equipment must comply with one of the provisions for basic protection, typically basic insulation, barriers or enclosures.

Basic insulation should be capable of withstanding any electrical, mechanical or other stresses that it may be expected to be subjected to in normal service. Consideration should therefore be given to the conditions that the electrical installation will experience, and the insulation provided should be suitable to maintain its insulation quality throughout its expected life.

Protection by a barrier or an enclosure is usually achieved by simply placing either a barrier in front of live parts to prevent contact, or the live parts being enclosed, preventing access to the live parts.

A degree of protection of at least IP2X or IPXXB is required by the Regulations where the barrier or enclosure is to provide basic protection. Furthermore the horizontal top surface of the enclosure is required to meet the requirements of at least IP4X or IPXXD degree of protection if the surface is readily accessible.

The table below summarizes the requirements

Applicable surface(s) of the enclosure or barrier	IP Code designation	Brief description of protection provided against access to live parts
All except a readily accessible top surface	IP2X or IPXXB	Protection against access to live parts with a finger or a solid object of 12.5 mm diameter and greater. Protection against access to live parts with a test finger at least 12 mm in diameter and 80 mm long.
Readily accessible top surface	IP4X or IPXXD	Protection against access to live parts with a straight wire or strip of more than 1.0 mm diameter or thickness and 100 mm long.

Where it is necessary to remove a barrier or open an enclosure, or to remove parts of enclosures, which may be required for maintenance for example, this shall only be possible by:

- the use of a key or tool, *or*
- an arrangement such as a door interlocked isolator is provided to prevent live parts being accessible, or
- an intermediate barrier being provided, affording a degree of protection of at least IP2X or IPXXB and only removable by the use of a tool.

4.0.7   Obstacles and Placing out of reach (417)

The protective measures of obstacles and placing out of reach provide basic protection only, and are for applications in installations with or without fault protection that are controlled and supervised by skilled or instructed persons.

4.1   Protection against thermal effects (Chapter 42)

A considerable number of fires are caused by the electrical installation. Common causes are overloaded cables, cables without adequate protection and loose or poor terminations. Other causes include:

- arcs
- harmonic currents
- failure of electrical equipment
- incorrect design
- poor workmanship
- insulation faults

Chapter 42 of *BS 7671* applies to electrical installations and equipment with regard to measures for the protection of people, livestock and property:

- against the harmful effects of heat or thermal radiation developed by electrical equipment
- against the ignition, combustion or degradation of materials
- against flames and smoke where a fire hazard could be propagated from an electrical installation to other nearby fire compartments, and
- against safety services being cut off by the failure of electrical equipment.

Within Chapter 42 there are three sections:

- Section 421 Protection against fire caused by electrical equipment
- Section 422 Precautions where particular risks of fire exist
- Section 423 Protection against burns

4.1.1 Protection against fire caused by electrical equipment

This section provides the requirements to help prevent the electrical installation presenting a fire hazard. It states that manufacturers' instructions must be complied with and that fixed electrical equipment should be selected and erected such that its temperature in normal operation will not cause a fire.

Any electrical equipment that may attain surface temperatures that could cause a fire hazard to adjacent materials, must be installed to prevent this.

This can be achieved by adequate screening, methods of dissipating heat or mounting a sufficient distance away from combustible objects.

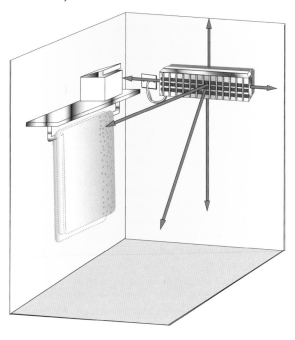

→ Indicates distance from heat source

Fig 4.10 Protection against fire

The construction of the enclosures used for electrical equipment must comply with the resistance to heat and fire requirements in an appropriate product standard.

An important requirement of Section 421 is that every termination of a live conductor or connection or joint between live conductors shall be contained within an enclosure selected in accordance with Regulation 526.5

This requirement is often overlooked and examples of connections made to luminaires and joints within the fixed wiring provide evidence that the requirements of this regulation have not been met. This also applies to extra-low voltage.

4.1.2 Precautions where particular risks of fire exist

In addition to the requirements of Sections 420 and 421, Section 422 outlines further precautions where a particular risk of fire exists.

Conditions for evacuation in an emergency

Within Section 422 there are requirements that restrict the routing of cables, type of wiring systems used and access to switchgear within escape routes. The density of occupation and the degree of difficulty of evacuation will influence the specific requirements.

This is particularly applicable to public buildings, high-rise buildings and buildings where specific conditions present evacuation problems, for example, hospitals and theatres.

Locations with risks of fire due to the nature of processed or stored materials

Locations such as flour mills, woodworking machinery workshops, grain silos and agricultural barns may provide an increased risk of fire. Any electrical equipment located within places which provide additional risks shall be kept at an adequate distance from combustible materials.

Any switchgear or control gear should be installed outside the location unless specific requirements are met (Regulation 422.3.3). Luminaires are particularly hazardous due to their surface temperature. A build up of wood dust on a luminaire could easily present a fire hazard. Regulation 422.3.8 provides the requirements for luminaires installed in such conditions.

4.1.3 Protection against burns

The maximum temperature of accessible parts of electrical equipment within arm's reach should be limited to protect persons against burns.

Excepting equipment for which a Harmonized Standard specifies a limiting temperature, the maximum temperatures given in Table 42.1 of *BS 7671* should not be exceeded.

Temperature limit under normal load conditions for an accessible part of equipment within arm's reach

Accessible part	Materials of accessible surfaces	Maximum temperature °C
A hand-held part	Metallic Non-metallic	55 65
A part intended to be touched but not hand-held	Metallic Non-metallic	70 80
A part which need not be touched for normal operation	Metallic Non-metallic	80 90

If the above temperatures are exceeded by accessible parts of equipment within arm's reach, even for a short period, appropriate guards must be fitted to prevent accidental contact.

4.2   Protection against overcurrent (Chapter 43)

Chapter 43 provides requirements for the protection of live conductors from the effects of overcurrent. The requirements are intended to protect persons, livestock and property from the hazards that occur when a circuit is carrying current in excess of its normal operating current

Regulation 430.3 states that 'A protective device shall be provided to break any current in the circuit conductors before such a current could cause a danger due to thermal or mechanical effects detrimental to insulation, connections, joints, terminations or the surroundings of the conductors'

Chapter 43 describes how live conductors are protected by one or more devices for the automatic disconnection of the supply in the event of overload current or fault current.

Overcurrent may be due to one of the following:

- **Overload** – an overcurrent occurring in a circuit which is electrically sound
- **Fault current** – one of two types:

i) Short circuit current – a fault of negligible impedance between live conductors

ii) Earth fault current – a fault current which flows to earth

Section 431 provides the requirements for the protection of line conductors. Detection of overcurrent should be provided for all line conductors and should cause disconnection of the conductor in which the overcurrent is detected, and not necessarily in other line conductors, unless the disconnection of one line conductor could cause danger or damage.

Although reference is made to the protection of line conductors, Section 431 provides requirements for protection of neutral conductors also.

In conventional single and three-phase installations, as the neutral conductor will normally be the same cross-sectional area as the line conductors, the overcurrent protective device in the line conductor will provide protection for the neutral conductor.

In three-phase installations with a reduced neutral cross-sectional area, the neutral shall be provided with protection which will disconnect the line conductors.

Published by NICEIC. © Electrical Safety Council (Jan 2008)

Where the presence of harmonic currents could cause the current-carrying capacity of the neutral to be exceeded, the neutral should be provided with protection which will disconnect the line conductors, and therefore protect the neutral conductor.

4.2.1   Nature of protective devices (Section 432)
Protection against both overload and fault current

A device providing protection against both overload and fault current shall be capable of breaking, and for a circuit-breaker making, any overcurrent up to and including the maximum prospective fault current at the point where the device is installed.

Protection against overload current only

Protection against overload current only is permissible, although the characteristics of the device used must be co-ordinated with the device providing fault current protection and have a breaking capacity in excess of the energy let-through of that device.

Characteristics of protective devices

The time/current characteristics of an overcurrent protective device shall comply with those specified by:

- *BS 88*
- *BS 1361*
- *BS 3036*
- *BS EN 60898*
- *BS EN 60947-2*
- *BS EN 61009-1*

The use of other devices is not excluded provided that their time/current characteristics provide equivalent levels of protection.

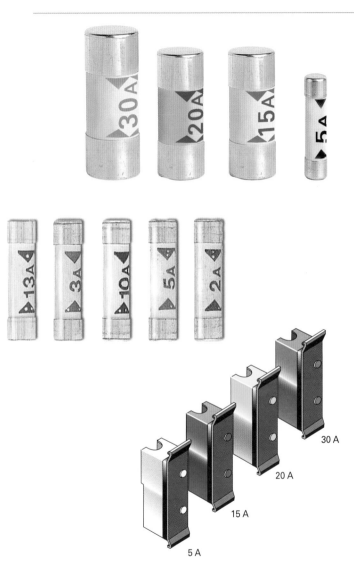

Fig 4.11 Protective devices

Co-ordination between conductor and overload protective device

Every circuit should be designed so that a small overload of long duration is unlikely to occur.

Should an overload occur, the protective device is designed to automatically disconnect the circuit. If overload protection was not provided, the temperature of the circuit conductors could rise excessively, possibly damaging the insulation, terminations and /or their surroundings.

To protect against such damage, the design of the circuit has to properly co-ordinate the current-carrying capacity of the conductors and the anticipated load current with the characteristics of the protective device.

Co-ordination will be met and comply with Regulation 433.1.1 if:

$$I_b \leq I_n \leq I_z$$

Where

I_b = design current of circuit.

I_n = rated current of protective device.

I_z = current-carrying capacity of the conductor.

Co-ordination will also be met and comply with Regulation 433.1.1 (ii) if:

$$I_2 \leq 1.45 \times I_z$$

Where

I_2 = the current ensuring effective operation of the device in the conventional time (e.g 0.4 or 5 seconds)

This means that the current causing effective operation of the protective device must not exceed 1.45 times the lowest current-carrying capacity (I_z) of any of the conductors in the circuit.

Regulation 433.3.1 provides circumstances where devices for protection against overload need not be provided.

Regulation 434.3 provides circumstances where devices for protection against fault current need not be provided.

Part 5
Selection and erection of
equipment

5.1   Common rules (Chapter 51)

General

Chapter 51 deals with the selection of equipment and its erection. It provides common rules for compliance with measures for protection for safety, requirements for proper functioning for intended use of the installation, and requirements appropriate to the external influences.

Every item of equipment shall be selected and erected in compliance with Chapter 51 and the other relevant parts of *BS 7671*.

BS 7671 now states that manufacturers' instructions should be taken into account.

All equipment should comply with the relevant British or Harmonized Standards appropriate to the intended use of the equipment. Equipment selected that is not covered by a British or Harmonized Standard must not result in a lesser degree of safety than that afforded by a British Standard, and must be recorded on the Electrical Installation Certificate.

Operational conditions and external influences

Every item of equipment must be suitable for:

- Voltage, nominal and the highest and lowest that may occur, and
- Current, design current and under fault conditions
- Frequency
- Power characteristics
- Compatibility, items of equipment selected must not cause harmful effects or impair the safety during normal service including switching operations.

External influences

All electrical installations are subject to one or more external influences, the most common being temperature, moisture, environmental conditions and the utilisation and construction of the building. Regulation 512.2.1 states that equipment must be of a design appropriate to the situation in which it is to be used or its mode of installation must take account of the conditions likely to be encountered.

Assessment of any external influences is necessary not only for proper functioning but also for the reliability of the measures of protection for safety.

Accessibility

Every item of equipment should be installed so that it can easily be operated, inspected and maintained and access provided to each connection. This facility must not be impaired by mounting equipment in an enclosure or a compartment.

Identification and notices

Section 514 provides the requirements for the identification of conductors and wiring systems including switchgear, and the requirements for any danger or warning notices that may be required.

The wiring should be arranged or marked so that it can be identified for inspection, testing, repair or alteration.

Selection and erection of equipment

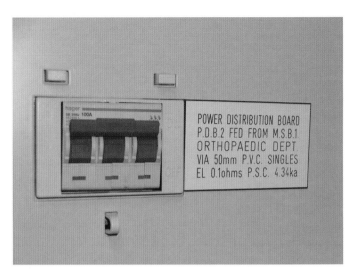

Fig 5.1 Example of indentification label

Identification of conductors and wiring systems

Where electrical conduit is used and it is necessary to distinguish it from other services, it should be coloured orange.

Cores of cables should be identified by:

- Colour
- Letter
- Number

The cores should be identified at their terminations and preferably throughout their length.

Table 51 of *BS 7671* reproduced below provides the requirements for identification of conductors.

TABLE 51 - Identification of conductors

Function		Colour	Alpha numeric
Protective conductors		Green-and-yellow	
Functional earthing conductor		Cream	
a.c. power circuit[1]			
Line of single-phase circuit		Brown	L
Neutral of single- or three-phase circuit		Blue	N
Line 1 of three-phase circuit		Brown	L1
Line 2 of three-phase circuit		Black	L2
Line 3 of three-phase circuit		Grey	L3
Two-wire unearthed d.c. power circuit			
Positive of two-wire circuit		Brown	L+
Negative of two-wire circuit		Grey	L-
Two-wire earthed d.c. power circuit			
Positive (of negative earthed) circuit		Brown	L+
Negative (of negative earthed) circuit[2]		Blue	M
Positive (of positive earthed) circuit[2]		Blue	M
Negative (of positive earthed) circuit		Grey	L-
Three-wire d.c. power circuit			
Outer positive of two-wire circuit derived from three-wire system		Brown	L+
Outer negative of two-wire circuit derived from three-wire system		Grey	L-
Positive of three-wire circuit		Brown	L+
Mid-wire of three-wire circuit[2][3]		Blue	M
Negative of three-wire circuit		Grey	L-
Control circuits, ELV and other applications			
Line conductor		Grey	L

	Brown		Orange	White
	Black		Yellow	Pink, or
	Red		Violet	Turquoise

Function		Colour	Alpha numeric
Neutral or mid-wire[4]		Blue	N or M

NOTES: [1] Power circuits include lighting circuits.
[2] M identifies either the mid-wire of a three-wire d.c. circuit, or the earthed conductor of a two-wire earthed dc circuit.
[3] Only the middle wire of three-wire circuits may be earthed.
[4] An earthed PELV conductor is blue.

Changes to the colour identification of conductors in fixed wiring were introduced by Amendment No 2 to *BS 7671* : 2001 on 31 March 2004. Appendix 7 of *BS 7671* provides further information regarding the changes to colour identification. Where newly installed cables interface with existing cables of pre-harmonized colours, the guidance of Appendix 7 of *BS 7671* should be followed.

Published by NICEIC. © Electrical Safety Council (Jan 2008)

Selection and erection of equipment

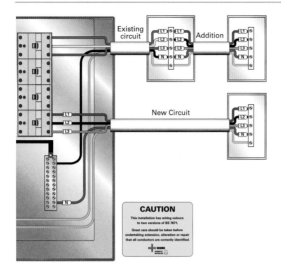

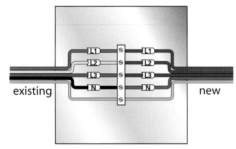

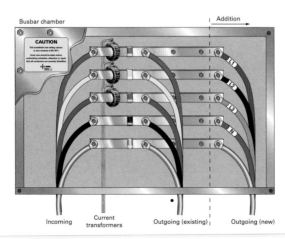

Fig 5.2 Illustration of interface between exsisting and new colours

Protective conductors must be coloured green-and-yellow as indicated in Table 51, and this combination is reserved solely for these conductors. The Regulations also state that apart from PEN conductors, single-core cables coloured green-and-yellow throughout their length should not be overmarked at their terminations.

Conductors with green and yellow colour identification must not be numbered apart from the purpose of circuit identification.

Common departures
1. Protective conductor not identified by the colours green-and-yellow
2. Cores of cables have not been correctly identified

Identification of protective devices

Regulation 514.8.1 provides the requirements for the identification of a protective device and states that 'A protective device shall be arranged and identified so that the circuit protected may be easily recognised.'

In practice it is not always possible to individually label protective devices and in these circumstances they may be identified by a durable chart or schedule fitted inside the cover, or adjacent to, the distribution board.

Regulation 514.9.1 stipulates the following requirements for the information that should be provided:

- the type and composition of each circuit, including points served, number and size of conductors, type of wiring, and
- method used for providing shock protection
- the information necessary for the identification of each device performing the functions of protection, isolation and switching, and its location, *and*

Selection and erection of equipment

- any circuit or equipment vulnerable to a typical test.

For simple installations the above information may be provided in a schedule, typically that which forms the 'schedule of circuit details' as part of the Electrical Installation Certificate. For more complex installations, more comprehensive information would be required.

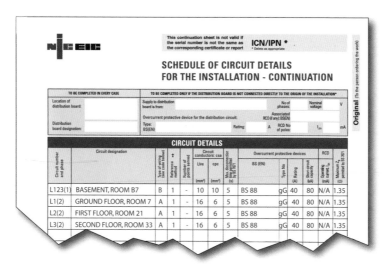

Fig 5.3 Example of a 'schedule of circuit details'

Common departures
1. Protective device has not been identified so the circuit protected can be recognised
2. A durable schedule has not been provided within or adjacent to the distribution board

Warning notices

Section 514 contains the requirements for the provision of notices. It should be noted that more specific notices are covered in other sections of *BS 7671*.

Voltage

A warning notice should be provided where within an item of equipment or enclosure, a nominal voltage exceeding 230 volts exists, and where the presence of such a voltage would not normally be expected. The warning notice must be visible before access is gained to a live part.

Warning notice – this enclosure contains circuits with 400 volts or 400 volts exist between this and adjacent electrical equipment

Fig 5.4 Example of voltage warning notice

Isolation

Where live parts are not capable of being isolated by a single device, and no interlocking arrangement is provided to ensure that all circuits concerned are isolated prior to gaining access, Regulation 514.11.1 requires that a durable warning notice should be provided.

If the location of each isolator is not obvious, information regarding the location should be provided as part of the notice.

Periodic inspection and testing

A notice must be provided, which is likely to remain legible throughout the life of the installation and fixed in a prominent position, at or near the origin of every installation, upon completion of the work carried out. The notice provides dates for the date the work was completed and the date recommended for the next inspection.

Selection and erection of equipment

> This installation should be periodically inspected
> and tested and a report on its condition obtained,
> as prescribed in the IEE Wiring Regulations BS 7671
> Requirements for Electrical Installations.
>
> Date of last Inspection ▇▇▇▇▇▇▇▇▇▇
>
> Recommended date of next inspection ▇▇▇▇▇▇
>
> N|CEIC
> APPROVED
> CONTRACTOR

Fig 5.5 Periodic inspection label

Where an installation incorporates an RCD, a notice shall be
fixed in a prominent position at or near the origin of the
installation stating that the 'Test' button should be operated
quarterly.

Earthing and bonding connections

A permanent label to *BS 951* with the words 'Safety
electrical connection – do not remove' must be permanently
fixed in a visible position at or near:

- the point of connection of every earthing conductor to an
  earth electrode, and
- the point of connection of every bonding conductor to an
  extraneous-conductive-part, and
- the main earth terminal where separate from main switchgear.

Fig 5.6 Earthing and bonding warning label

Non standard colours

If alterations or additions are made to an existing installation and core colours of both old and new are present, a warning notice must be fitted at or near the appropriate distribution board with the following wording:

CAUTION

This installation has wiring colours to two versions of BS 7671.

Great care should be taken before undertaking extension, alteration or repair that all conductors are correctly identified.

Fig 5.7 Mixed wiring colours warning notice

Common departures
1. A notice indicating live parts are not capable of isolation by a single device has been omitted
2. A periodic inspection and test label has not been fitted at or near the installation origin
3. An RCD test notice has been omitted
4. A warning notice has not been fitted to earthing/bonding connections
5. A warning notice has not been fitted to indicate non-standard colours. Wiring colours of two versions of *BS 7671*

Prevention of mutual detrimental influences

The selection and erection of electrical equipment must take into account any external influences and also influences that are mutually detrimental. The designer and installer must therefore consider the external influences that may be applicable and also other mutually detrimental influences, such as other services and structural components of the building that may affect the electrical installation.

Selection and erection of equipment

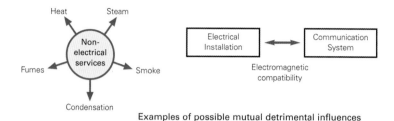

Examples of possible mutual detrimental influences

Fig 5.8 Examples of possible mutual detrimental influences.

Where equipment or circuits are carrying current of different types or voltages, (such as a.c. and d.c.) and are grouped within a common assembly such as a switchboard or control desk, they should be effectively segregated to avoid mutual detrimental influence.

Common departures
1. Wiring system is located in too close a proximity to a non-electrical service

5.2   Selection and erection of wiring systems (Chapter 52)

The correct selection and erection of a wiring system is important to ensure that it is suitable for its intended purpose and that consideration has been given to any external influences that the wiring system may be subjected to.

The term 'wiring system' covers containment for the installed cables, e.g. trunking, conduit, cable tray, basket tray etc. and the installed cables, single-core or multicore cable, sheathed or non-sheathed.

Regulation 520.3 states that consideration should be given to the application of the fundamental principles of Chapter 13 as it applies to:

- cables and conductors
- their connections, terminations and/or jointing
- their associated supports or suspensions and
- their enclosure or methods of protection against external influences

Types of wiring system

The installation method of a wiring system in relation to the type of conductor or cable used should be in accordance with Table 4A1, provided any external influences have been taken into account.

As an example from Table 4A1, non-sheathed cables are not permitted to be clipped direct, but are permitted in conduit or trunking systems.

The installation method of a wiring system in relation to the situation concerned should be in accordance with Table 4A2, extracts of which are shown below. Other methods of installation of cables, conductors and busbars are permitted provided they meet the requirements of Chapter 52.

Busbar trunking systems commonly used in buildings to distribute electricity, rising mains or overhead busbars for example, must comply with *BS EN 60439-2* and should be installed in accordance with manufacturers' instructions taking account of external influences.

Published by NICEIC. © Electrical Safety Council (Jan 2008)

Selection and erection of equipment

A.C. circuits - electromagnetic effects

The electromagnetic effects from incorrectly installed cables of a.c. circuits can cause heat to be generated in the metal of ferromagnetic enclosures, such as conduit or equipment enclosures. To prevent this, *BS 7671* requires the following:

a) Single-core cables armoured with steel wire or steel tape should not be used for an a.c. circuit

b) The conductors of an a.c. circuit installed in a ferromagnetic enclosure shall be arranged so that all line conductors and the neutral conductor, if any, and the appropriate protective conductor are contained in the same enclosure

c) Where such conductors enter a ferrous enclosure they should be arranged such that the conductors are only collectively surrounded by ferrous material. (see illustration below)

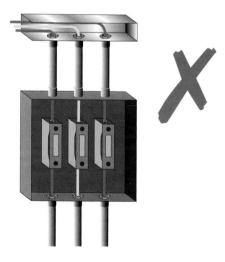

Fig 5.9 Conductors incorrectly entering a ferrous enclosure.

Conduit, ducting, trunking, tray and ladder systems

Two or more circuits are allowed in the same conduit, ducting or trunking system provided the requirements of section 528 are met. Section 528 deals with the proximity of wiring systems to other services and detrimental effects between wiring systems.

Circuit arrangements

Each part of a circuit should be arranged such that conductors are not distributed over different multi-core cables, conduits or other wiring systems. If multi-core cables are installed in parallel, then each cable must contain one conductor of each line.

The line and neutral conductor of each final circuit must be electrically separate from that of every other final circuit. This requirement is to prevent the indirect energising of a final circuit intended to be isolated.

Use of flexible cables or cords

Where a wiring system is selected that supplies equipment that is intended to be moved, flexible cables or cords must be utilised. Stationary equipment that may be moved temporarily for the purpose of cleaning or connecting, e.g. cooking equipment, may be supplied by non-flexible cables.

Any equipment that is subject to vibration should also be supplied by a flexible cable or cord.

Installation of cables

Non-sheathed cables for fixed wiring must be enclosed in conduit, ducting or trunking. This requirement does not apply to protective conductors complying with Section 543. The cable trunking system must provide at least the degree of protection IP4X or IPXXD and the cover must only be removable by a tool or by deliberate action.

Selection and erection of wiring systems in relation to external influences

When selecting a wiring system it is important that all possible detrimental effects are considered in all appropriate parts of the wiring system. Particular care should be taken at changes in direction and where wiring enters into equipment.

The designer and installer should consider the external influences identified within Section 522 which are:

- Ambient temperature (AA)
- External heat sources
- Presence of water (AD) or high humidity (AB)
- Presence of solid foreign bodies (AE)
- Presence or corrosive or polluting substances (AF)
- Impact (AG)
- Vibration (AH)
- Other mechanical stresses (AJ)
- Presence of flora and/or mould growth (AK)
- Presence of fauna (AL)
- Solar radiation (AN) and ultraviolet radiation
- Seismic effects (AP)
- Wind (AS)
- Nature of processed or stored materials (BE)
- Building design (CB)

Within this section of the 'Toolbox Guide' the most common external influences are covered, for a more detailed approach Appendix 5 of *BS 7671* should be consulted.

Ambient temperature

Wiring systems must be selected for the highest and lowest ambient local temperatures they are likely to encounter. Cables have a limiting temperature in normal operation (Table 52.1 overleaf) and a limiting temperature under fault conditions. These values must not be exceeded.

Table 52.1 Maximum operating temperatures for types of cable insulation

Type of insulation	Temperature limit *
Thermoplastic	70 °C at the conductor
Thermosetting	90 °C at the conductor *
Mineral (Thermoplastic covered or bare exposed to touch)	70 °C at the sheath
Mineral (bare not exposed to touch and not in contact with combustible material)	105 °C at the sheath *

* There are specific notes provided in *BS 7671* with regard to the above temperatures.

External heat sources

Heat from an external source can be detrimental to the wiring system and an effective method of protection must be provided such as:

- shielding
- placing sufficiently far from the heat source
- selecting a system with due regard for the additional temperature rise which may occur
- local reinforcement or substitution of insulating material

Cables and flexible cords that are installed inside accessories, appliances or luminaires must be suitable for the temperatures likely to be encountered. Additional insulation by utilising heat resistant sleeving may be required, for example when connecting cooking appliances, heaters or light fittings.

Selection and erection of equipment

Presence of solid foreign bodies (AE)

This term relates to objects from particles of dust to larger objects that may have an effect on the wiring system or electrical equipment.

Dust can be a particular problem as it can adversely affect the mechanical operation of certain electrical equipment and it can provide an insulator when allowed to settle in any quantity on equipment. This could cause local overheating.

Impact (AG)

Another relatively common external influence is where a wiring system may be subject to impact. An example of this may be in a warehouse where boxes and pallets are moved and could come into contact with the electrical installation. Precautions would have to be taken to select a wiring system that would be able to withstand such detrimental influences.

Cables buried in a floor

Under floor trunking or ducting systems buried in the floor screed are also liable to mechanical damage due to the loads been placed on the floor caused by the intended use and should, therefore, be sufficiently protected.

Cables installed under floors or above a ceiling

Another area where mechanical protection needs careful consideration is where a wiring system is installed under a floor or above a ceiling. Cables in this situation should be run in such a position that they are not liable to damage by contact with the floor or the ceiling or their fixings. The diagram overleaf illustrates the requirements. Generally, the cables should either be 50 mm from the top, or bottom as appropriate, of the joist or batten or incorporate an earthed armour or screen or be provided with mechanical protection to prevent the penetration of the cable by nails, screws and the like.

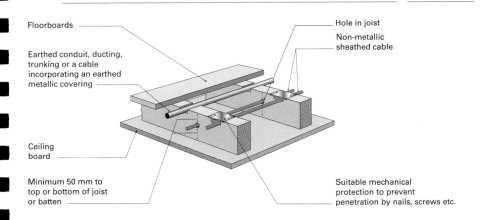

Floorboards

Earthed conduit, ducting, trunking or a cable incorporating an earthed metallic covering

Ceiling board

Minimum 50 mm to top or bottom of joist or batten

Hole in joist

Non-metallic sheathed cable

Suitable mechanical protection to prevent penetration by nails, screws etc.

Fig 5.10 Protection for cables passing through or over a joist

Where wiring systems penetrate an element of building construction which is intended to be load bearing the integrity of the bearing element must be assured after such penetration.

Cables concealed in walls or partitions

It is extremely important that the requirements relating to the protection of cables in walls and partitions are fully understood. Damage to cables in walls or partitions can often occur, for example, where fixings are being made and drills, screws or nails penetrate the cables. The Regulations outlining the requirements offer several options which must be considered carefully. In many cases where the installation is not intended to be under the supervision of a skilled or instructed person, concealed cables will require additional protection by means of an RCD having the characteristics specified in Regulation 415.1.1

RCD protection not required

Where a cable is concealed in a wall or partition deeper than 50 mm from the surface of the wall or partition no further protection is required (apart from the exemptions overleaf)

Selection and erection of equipment

Where cables are installed at a depth of **less than 50 mm** from the surface of a wall or partition and one of the following requirements are met, RCD protection is not required:

- the cable must incorporate an earthed metallic covering or
- the cable must be enclosed in earthed conduit satisfying the requirements for a protective conductor or
- the cable must be enclosed in earthed trunking or ducting satisfying the requirements for a protective conductor or
- the cable must be mechanically protected against damage sufficient to provide protection against the penetration by nails, screws and the like.

RCD protection is required

Where cables are installed at a depth of less than 50mm deep, and the protective methods detailed above are not used, an RCD (having the characteristics specified in Regulation 415.1.1) is required.

The *cable zones* which were an important requirement of the 16th edition of *BS 7671* are still just as relevant, but in addition, cables will now require RCD protection even where they are run in the specified cable zones, unless the installation is intended to be under the supervision of a skilled or instructed person.

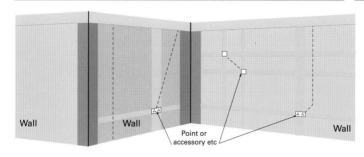

Wall   Wall   Wall

Point or accessory etc

Zone within 150 mm of the top of the wall

Zone within 150 mm of an angle formed by adjacent walls

Only in a straight run either horizontally or vertically to a point, accessory or switchgear to which the cable is connected

- - - Example of route where suitable mechanical protection is required for cable

Where cables are less than 50 mm from the surface RCD protection will be required (unless the installation is intended to be under the supervision of a skilled or instructed person)

Fig 5.11 Zones for concealed cables in walls and partitions

In addition to the above requirements for zones, where the location of the accessory, point or switchgear can be determined from the reverse side, a zone formed on one side of a wall or partition of 100 mm thickness or less extends to the reverse side. This is illustrated below.

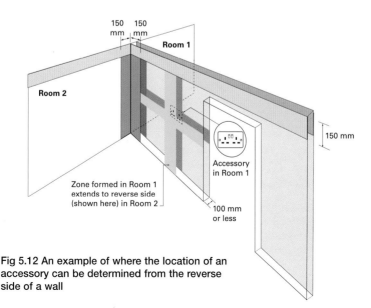

150 mm | 150 mm

Room 1

Room 2

150 mm

Accessory in Room 1

Zone formed in Room 1 extends to reverse side (shown here) in Room 2

100 mm or less

Fig 5.12 An example of where the location of an accessory can be determined from the reverse side of a wall

Selection and erection of equipment

Finally, **RCD protection is also required where** cables are concealed in a wall or partition and the **internal construction of the walls or partition include metallic parts** (other than metallic fixings e.g. screws or nails). This requirement applies irrespective of the depth of the cable from a surface of the wall or partition. There is an exemption to this requirement where the installation is intended to be under the supervision of a skilled or instructed person or not.

Summary of cables concealed in walls or partitions and *not requiring* RCD protection

Where more than 50 mm from the surface of a wall or partition. (However, see walls or partitions the internal construction of which includes metallic parts below*)
Where incorporating an earthed metallic covering as specified in Regulation 522.6.(i)
Where enclosed in earthed conduit as specified in Regulation 522.6 (ii)
Where enclosed in earthed trunking or ducting as specified in Regulation 522.6 (iii)
Where mechanically protected as specified in Regulation 522.6 (iv)
Where installed in the zones specified in Regulation 522.6 (v) and the installation is intended to be under the supervision of a skilled or instructed person.
*Where cables are concealed in a wall or partition where the internal construction include metallic parts (other than metallic fixings e.g. screws or nails) and the installation is intended to be under the supervision of a skilled or instructed person.

Summary of cables concealed in walls or partitions *requiring* RCD protection

Where cables are concealed less than 50 mm from the surface of a wall or partition, and where they are not incorporating an earthed metallic covering or enclosed in earthed conduit, trunking or ducting (as specified in Regulation 522.6) and where they are not intended to be under the supervision of a skilled or instructed person.

Where cables are concealed in a wall or partition where the internal construction include metallic parts (other than metallic fixings e.g. screws or nails) and the installation is not intended to be under the supervision of a skilled or instructed person.

Vibration (AH)

A wiring system supported by or fixed to a structure or equipment subject to vibration could eventually break or come loose, and terminations are vulnerable as cables vibrate and place additional stress on terminations. The use of flexible cables will usually provide the necessary protection against vibration.

Light fittings installed within a ceiling grid may be subject to vibration and therefore cables with flexible cores should be used in such circumstances.

Other mechanical stresses (AJ)

A wiring system should be selected and erected to avoid during installation, use or maintenance, damage to the sheath or insulation of cables and their terminations. One way to meet this requirement is to protect the cables from sharp edges in containment systems or accessories by the use of channelling, grommets or grommet strip.

Selection and erection of equipment

Fig 5.13 Channelling and grommet used to protect cables prior to plastering

Where conduit or ducting systems are buried in the structure of the building, they should be completely erected between access points before the cables are drawn in. Wiring systems intended for the drawing in and out of conductors or cables require adequate access to allow this operation.

The radius of bends, within wiring systems, should be such that conductors or cables do not suffer damage and terminals are not stressed. Cables and conductors must be supported so that they do not suffer damage or strain from the weight of the cable itself (see also Section 526 of *BS 7671*). Manufacturers' recommendations should be followed in relation to supports for cables.

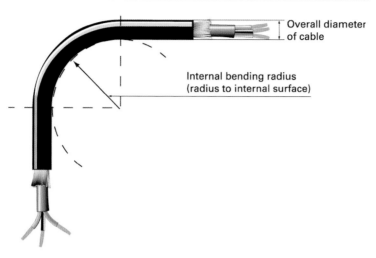

Fig 5.14 Internal bending radius and overall
diameter of a cable

Where cables are buried in the ground, unless they are
installed within a conduit or duct, the cable must
incorporate earthed armour or metal sheath, or both,
suitable for use as a protective conductor. The location of
buried cables should be marked by cable covers or
marking tape, and cables should be buried at a suitable
depth to avoid damage.

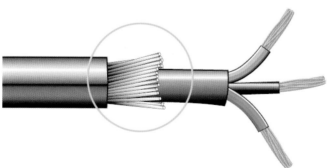

Fig 5.15 Armoured cable

Published by NICEIC. © Electrical Safety Council (Jan 2008)

Selection and erection of equipment

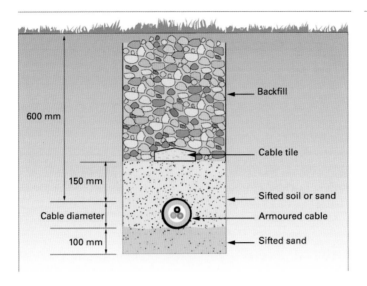

Fig 5.16 Typical section through a buried wiring system

Wiring systems require protection generally from; sharp edges on cable supports and enclosures, damage to cables or conductors from any fixing means and damage from movement in any expansion joints that the wiring system passes across. In addition to the Regulations relating to damage to cables and conductors, Regulation 522.8.14 requires that no wiring system should penetrate an element of the building construction, which is intended to be load-bearing, unless the integrity of the load-bearing element can be assured after such penetration.

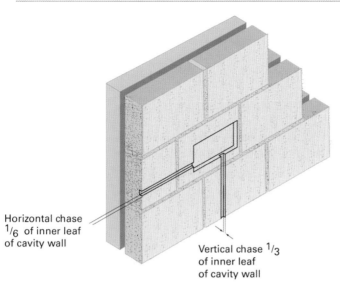

Horizontal chase
$^1/_6$ of inner leaf
of cavity wall

Vertical chase $^1/_3$
of inner leaf
of cavity wall

Fig 5.17 Restrictions on the penetration of building construction element (wall)

Common departures
1. Bending radius of wiring system liable to cause damage
2. Cable in floor/ceiling not at a depth of 50 mm to avoid mechanical damage
3. Cable concealed in a wall or partition at a depth less than 50 mm not mechanically protected / outside prescribed zones
4. Wiring system has not been protected against mechanical damage due to impact
5. Wiring system has not been protected against mechanical damage to sheath and insulation during installation, use and maintenance
6. Wiring system not adequately supported and liable to mechanical strain

Presence of fauna (AL)

A common problem for wiring systems, installed where there is a presence of fauna, is rodents causing damage to the installed cables. Mechanical protection should be provided or protection given to the wiring system to prevent such damage.

Selection and erection of equipment

Electrical installations on farms may be more vulnerable not only from the presence of fauna but from impact and animal urine providing additional detrimental influences.

Solar radiation (AN) and ultraviolet radiation

A wiring system installed where significant solar radiation can be expected should be suitable for the conditions that are expected. Solar radiation can cause degradation of cable sheaths, and in addition to this can affect the current-carrying capacity of the cable, due to the increased ambient temperature.

Building design (CB)

Where the design of the building allows structural movement, the cable support and protection system should be selected and erected to allow for the expected movement. Flexible wiring systems should be installed in structures intended to move.

Current-carrying capacities of cables

The current, including any harmonic current, to be carried by any conductor for sustained periods during normal operation shall be such that the appropriate temperature limit specified in Table 52.1 of *BS 7671* is not exceeded.

The current-carrying capacity of cables and their cross-sectional area, along with voltage drop, are to be considered together. Detailed requirements for the calculation of conductor size are provided in Appendix 4 of *BS 7671*. Sample calculations are provided in the Appendices of this guide.

The current-carrying capacity of a cable depends upon a number of conditions. When designing an electrical installation and selecting cables the design process will need to consider the conditions in which the cables will be installed, and also the effect the installed conditions have on current-carrying capacity.

Method of installation

The method of installation will affect the rate of heat emission and therefore the current-carrying capacity of the cable.

The current-carrying capacity of a cable clipped direct to a surface is generally higher than that of the same cable enclosed in conduit, as the enclosure inhibits the escape of heat from the cable.

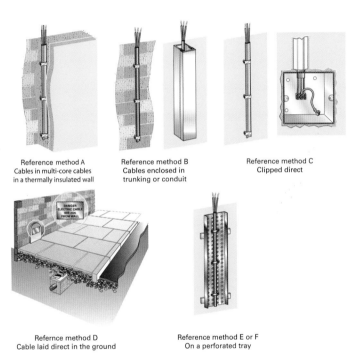

Reference method A
Cables in multi-core cables
in a thermally insulated wall

Reference method B
Cables enclosed in
trunking or conduit

Reference method C
Clipped direct

Refernce method D
Cable laid direct in the ground

Reference method E or F
On a perforated tray

Fig 5.18 Commonly used methods of cable installation

The different installation methods and their related reference method codes, are listed within Appendix 4 (Table 4A2). As it is important to ascertain the intended installation method as part of the cable selection process, reference should be made to this table. A summary of the typical installation methods is provided in the following table.

Selection and erection of equipment

Typical installation methods and related reference methods

Installation method description	Reference methods
Cables in conduit in a thermally insulated wall. Multicore cables direct in a thermally insulated wall.(For flat twin and earth cables in thermal insulation see Table 4A2) Non-sheathed cables in mouldings, architraves etc.	A
Cables in conduit, trunking, ducting or building voids. Single-core or multicore cables fixed directly under a wooden or masonry ceiling.	B
Clipped direct (including single-core or multicore cable direct in masonry).	C
Cables laid direct in ground or in ductings in ground.	D
Cables on perforated tray, brackets, wire-mesh tray, ladder, suspended from a wire or harness or spaced from a wall (more than 3 x cable diameter)	E or F
Flat twin and earth cables in thermal insulation (see Table 4A2)	100, 101,102 & 103 for cable type covered by 4D5 (Flat twin and earth cables)

Ambient temperature

The higher the ambient temperature of the location in which the cable is installed, the lower the current-carrying capacity of the cable. The current-carrying capacities in Appendix 4 are based on ambient temperatures for:

* Non-sheathed and sheathed cables in air 30 °C
* Buried cables, either directly in the soil or in ducts in the ground 20 °C

Where ambient temperatures are different to the above values, the appropriate factors have to be applied from Appendix 4.

Grouping of cables and conductors

Cables within many electrical installations are grouped together in common containment or clipped together on a common surface.

Where loaded conductors are grouped together, the current-carrying capacity of all the conductors is reduced. This reduction in current-carrying capacity is due to the mutual heating effect and the factor used to take this effect into account is referred to as the grouping factor.

Table 4C1 in appendix 4 of *BS 7671* provides the relevant factors to be used when calculating the current-carrying capacity of conductors that are grouped with other cables.

If it is known that a particular conductor is expected to carry no more than 30% of its grouped current-carrying capacity it may be ignored for the purpose of obtaining the rating factor for the rest of the group.

Cables in thermal insulation

Thermally insulating material is frequently used in walls or ceilings of buildings, but such material reduces the current-carrying capacity of any cable it may cover. The designer should take this into account and take steps to ensure that the current-carrying capacity of a cable will remain sufficient. Failure to take this into consideration may result in a cable that is covered in thermal insulation exceeding its rated value, such as 70 °C for thermoplastic (pvc) insulated conductors.

Cables installed in or adjacent to thermal insulation are to be considered differently, as the cable may be installed being in contact with a thermally conductive surface on one side or totally surrounded by thermal insulation.

Appendix 4 of *BS 7671* provides current-carrying capacities for cables installed in or adjacent to thermal insulation.

Selection and erection of equipment

Where a single cable is to be totally surrounded by thermal insulation for less than 0.5 m the current-carrying capacity of the cable shall be reduced by application of the derating factors in Table 52.2 of *BS 7671* shown below.

Length in insulation (mm)	Derating factor
50	0.88
100	0.78
200	0.63
400	0.51

Voltage drop in consumers' installations

When circuit conductors carry load current, a voltage drop is produced in them, which means that the voltage at the load end of the circuit will be less than that at the supply end. It is necessary to limit the voltage drop in a circuit so that the safe and satisfactory operation of current-using equipment supplied by the circuit is not impaired.

The factors that affect voltage drop are:

- conductor cross-sectional area
- type of cable
- circuit current
- length of conductor

The total voltage drop recommended for an electrical installation is given in Appendix 12 of *BS 7671* an extract of which is given below.

Voltage drop

Description	Lighting	Other uses
(i) Low voltage installations supplied directly from a public low voltage distribution system	3%	5%
(ii) Low voltage installation supplied from private LV supply (*)	6%	8%
(*) The voltage drop within each final circuit should not exceed the values given in (i)		
Where the wiring systems of the installation are longer than 100 m, the voltage drops indicated above may be increased by 0.005% per meter of the wiring system beyond 100 m, without this increase being greater than 0.5%.		
The voltage drop is determined from the demand by the current-using equipment, applying diversity factors where applicable, or from the value of the design current of the circuit.		
Note 1: A greater voltage drop may be acceptable for a motor circuit during starting and for other equipment with a high inrush current provided that in both cases it is ensured that the voltage variations remain within the limits specified in the relevant equipment standard.		
Note 2: The following temporary conditions are excluded: - voltage transients - voltage variation due to abnormal operation		
Voltage drops may be determined from Appendix 4 – Current-carrying capacity and voltage drop for cables and flexible cords		

Common departures
1. Cable in contact with thermal insulation has not been derated
2. Voltage drop exceeds that allowable.

Published by NICEIC. © Electrical Safety Council (Jan 2008)

Selection and erection of equipment

Electrical connections

The integrity of the electrical installation relies upon the quality of any joints or terminations. Regulation 526.1 states that every connection between conductors or between a conductor and other equipment shall provide durable electrical continuity and adequate mechanical strength and protection.

Examples of means of connection include a terminal of an accessory, a joint box, an item of switchgear or a compression type lug. The means of connection must take into account the following as appropriate:

- the material of the conductor and its insulation
- the number and shape of the wires forming the conductor
- the cross-sectional area of the conductor
- the number of conductors to be connected together
- the temperature attained at the terminals in normal service such that the effectiveness of the insulation of the conductors connected to them is not impaired
- where a soldered connection is used, the design must take account of creep, mechanical stress and temperature rise under fault current conditions
- the provision of adequate locking arrangements in situations subject to vibration or thermal cycling

Manufacturers' guidance must also be observed in terms of limitations of the equipment and installation guidance.

Accessibility of connections

With certain exceptions, electrical connections (joints and terminations) should be accessible for inspection, testing and maintenance. The connections should be in a location where they can be reasonably reached and where there is adequate working space. Where the connections are housed in an enclosure, it should include a detachable cover or other suitable means of opening.

Enclosures must meet the requirements of the appropriate IP code.

An example of an exemption to accessibility of connection would be a joint designed to be buried in the ground.

Where connections are made in places like roof spaces or within inter-floor spaces, provision should be made for access and their location recorded for future use. Typically this information should be provided within the operation and maintenance manuals and appended to the Electrical Installation Certificate.

Regulation 526.5 requires every connection in a live conductor or a PEN conductor to be made within one of the following types of enclosure, or a combination of them:

- A suitable accessory, such as a lighting switch or socket-outlet
- An equipment enclosure, such as a luminaire *or* distribution board
- An enclosure partly formed or completed with building material which is non-combustible

All enclosures must comply with the appropriate product standard and provide adequate protection from mechanical damage and any other external influences likely to be encountered.

The mechanical protection afforded by the sheath of PVC sheathed cables must enter completely into the enclosure to ensure its mechanical integrity. Standard non-sheathed cables run in conduit and trunking are also required to be enclosed.

Selection and erection of equipment

Common departures
1. Connections do not provide durable electrical continuity and mechanical strength
2. Terminations are not enclosed in a prescribed enclosure
3. Connections are not accessible for inspection, testing and maintenance
4. Equipment not arranged to give access to connections
5. Inadequate access to parts of the wiring system requiring maintenance

Selection and erection of wiring systems to minimise the spread of fire.

Section 527 of *BS 7671* provides the requirements relating to the selection and erection of wiring systems such that the risk of spread of fire is kept to a minimum. Two aspects in relation to the risk of spread of fire are considered:

- precautions within a fire-segregated compartment
- the sealing of wiring system penetrations

Wiring systems must be installed so that the general building structure performance and fire safety are not reduced. The installation of wiring systems should follow manufacturers' guidance.

Cables that comply with *BS EN 60332-1-2* may be installed without special precautions. The most common cables that meet this requirement include:

- Thermoplastic (PVC) to *BS 6004*
- Thermosetting (XLPE) to *BS 7211*
- Thermosetting to *BS 5467*
- Flexible cords to *BS 6500*

Sealing of wiring penetrations

Where a wiring system passes through a building element that has a specific fire resistant property, the openings made are likely to compromise the ability of that element to resist the spread of fire. In order to maintain this integrity, wiring systems that pass through such elements will need to be sealed after their installation.

In addition to the external sealing requirements, the internal areas of trunking and larger conduit systems may also require sealing. Intumescent seals have the capacity to resist the spread of fire for between 1 and 4 hours, depending on their rating, and expand as they are heated to seal gaps or openings.

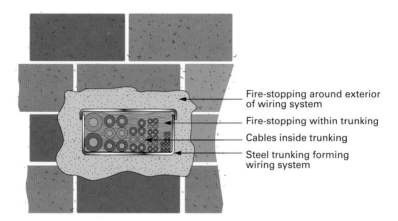

Fire-stopping around exterior of wiring system

Fire-stopping within trunking

Cables inside trunking

Steel trunking forming wiring system

Fig 5.19 A seal within a trunking system

In addition to the above requirements for the sealing of wiring systems, reducing the risk of spread of fire may have to be considered where accessories and electrical equipment is installed. An example of this is where recessed light fittings are installed in a ceiling. In some situations an intumescent cover may be required to ensure the ceiling fire integrity is maintained.

Selection and erection of equipment

Common departures
1. Fixed equipment gives rise to danger to adjacent material from thermal effects
2. Fixed equipment mounted such that heat is not dissipated
3. Building element raised to dangerous temperature from focussed heat of fixed equipment
4. Luminaire not suitable for mounting on combustible material
5. Wiring systems heat dissipation adversely effected by accumulation of dust / substance
6. Wiring system not sealed internally to maintain fire resistance
7. Electrical equipment not selected / erected to prevent fire in the event of a temperature rise

Proximity of wiring systems to other services

Circuits of voltage Band I and Band II must not be contained in the same wiring system as a circuit of nominal voltage exceeding that of low voltage and a Band I circuit must not be contained in the same wiring system as a Band II circuit, except where one of the following methods are adopted:

- every cable or conductor is insulated for the highest voltage present
- each conductor of a miulticore cable is insulated for the highest voltage present in the cable
- the cables are insulated for their system voltage and insulated in their separate compartment of a cable ducting or cable trunking system
- the cables are installed on a cable tray system where physical separation is provided
- a separate conduit, trunking or ducting system is employed
- for a multicore cable or cord, the cores of a Band I circuit should be separated from the cores of the Band II circuit by an earthed metal screen of equivalent current-carrying capacity to that of the largest core of the Band II circuit.

Designers and installers should also refer to the relevant British Standards for Fire Alarm systems, Emergency Lighting and Lightning Protection systems regarding the separation and segregation of safety circuits.

Proximity of non-electrical services

A wiring system should preferably be located away from non-electrical services but in some circumstances this is unavoidable. Wiring systems should not be installed in the vicinity of services that produce heat, smoke or fumes likely to be detrimental to the wiring, unless protected by shielding for example. Such shielding must not affect the dissipation of heat from the wiring.

Cables should be installed so that they are not exposed to any harmful influence by the normal operation of any adjacent services.

Where a wiring system is routed below services likely to cause condensation, precautions must be taken to protect the wiring.

If the wiring system is installed in close proximity to other services, then the following conditions should be met

- the wiring system is to be suitably protected against the hazards likely to arise from the presence of the non-electrical service in normal use, *and*
- fault protection is to be afforded in accordance with the requirements of Section 411, non-electrical metallic services being considered as extraneous-conductive-parts.

Lift shafts

In buildings where there is a lift shaft, or a shaft for a hoist, the only cables that should be run in the shaft are those which form part of the lift installation. Lift shafts should not be used as service risers.

Selection and erection of equipment

Selection and erection of wiring systems in relation to maintainability, including cleaning.

The electrical installation will require maintenance over time and the designer and installer must take account of this by the provision for future maintenance, to allow the installation to be maintained and kept in a safe condition throughout its life.

Where it is necessary to remove a protective measure in order to carry out maintenance, the protective measure must be able to be reinstated without reduction of the degree of protection originally intended.

Provision should be made for safe and adequate access to all parts of a wiring system which may require maintenance.

5.3   Protection, isolation, switching, control and monitoring. (Chapter 53)

Chapter 53 deals with the requirements to provide compliance with the measures for protection for safety, the requirements for proper functioning for the intended use of the installation, and the requirements appropriate to the external influences foreseen.

Fixing of equipment

Equipment should be fixed in accordance with manufacturer's instructions in such a way that connections between wiring and equipment should not be subject to undue stress or strain from the normal use of the equipment.

Unenclosed equipment should be mounted in an enclosure which complies with the relevant British Standard and fixed properly to the fabric of the building. Socket-outlets and similar accessories should be fitted to a mounting box complying with *BS 4662, BS 5733* or *BS EN 60670-1*

Wherever equipment is fixed on cable trunking, skirting trunking or in mouldings, it must not be fixed on covers which can be removed inadvertently.

Overcurrent protective devices

In TN and TT systems, overcurrent protective devices, where they are used for fault protection, should be selected and erected in order to comply with the requirements of Chapter 41.

Residual current devices (RCD)

General

Where RCDs are used they should:

- be capable of disconnecting all line conductors at substantially the same time
- have a rated residual operating current to comply with the requirements of section 411 as appropriate to the type of system earthing
- be selected and the electrical circuits be sub-divided so that any protective conductor current in normal operation of the connected loads will be unlikely to cause unnecessary tripping
- be located so that its operation will not be impaired by magnetic fields caused by other equipment
- if used for fault protection, be capable of withstanding, without damage, the thermal and mechanical stresses to which it is likely to be subjected by a fault occurring on the load side of the point at which it is installed
- provide discrimination in their operation, if necessary to prevent danger, where more than one device is installed

Selection and erection of equipment

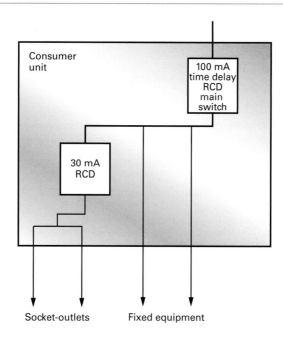

Fig 5.20 RCDs in series – use of time delay to provide discrimination

RCDs in a TN system

An RCD may be required in a TN system where the requirements of Regulation 411.4.5 cannot be met, such as a circuit that does not meet the requirements of maximum earth fault loop impedance. In such circumstances the exposed-conductive-parts of that part of the installation should be connected to the TN earthing system protective conductor, or to a separate earth electrode, which affords an impedance that is sufficiently low to ensure operation of the RCD.

RCDs in a TT system

If an installation which is part of a TT system is protected by a single RCD, then either:

• the RCD should be located at the origin of the installation, or

- the part of the installation between the origin and the RCD complies with the requirements for the protection by the use of class II equipment or equivalent insulation.

Protection against the risk of fire

In installations where there may be additional risk of fire, for example an agricultural installation, an RCD may be used for fault protection. In such installations, protection is required against the consequences of fault currents in a wiring system, and the subsequent fire risk, and the circuit must either

- be protected by an RCD for fault protection, which is installed at the origin of the circuit, switching all live conductors, and have a rated residual operating current not exceeding 300 mA, *or*
- be continuously monitored by an insulation monitoring device.

In any installation where an RCD is installed, the designer must consider the effects of unwanted tripping which sometimes arises with a 30 mA device. It may be necessary to utilise individual RCBOs (combined RCD and overcurrent device) as opposed to protecting several circuits with a single RCD. *BS 7671* requires that the installation be divided into circuits as necessary to avoid danger or inconvenience in the event of a fault.

Isolation and switching

Every electrical installation shall be provided with means of isolation and switching for the prevention or removal of dangers, functional switching and control.

Isolation and switching refers to four distinct operating functions

- Isolation
- Switching off for mechanical maintenance

Selection and erection of equipment

- Emergency switching
- Functional switching

Isolation

General points

The purpose of isolation is to provide protection for a skilled person engaged in electrical work. Once equipment has been securely isolated the skilled person should be able to safely access parts that would otherwise be live, without the risk of danger from electric shock.

Every circuit shall be capable of being isolated from each of the live supply conductors.

A suitable means must be provided to prevent the supply being unintentionally or inadvertently energised.

Working safely within the 'Electricity at Work Regulations' requires 'safe isolation' to be carried out. Part of the safe isolation procedure is to lock off the isolator thus preventing the supply being inadvertently energised.

Fig 5.21 A circuit breaker - locked off

The position of the contacts or other means of isolation should be either externally visible or clearly indicated.

A device used for isolation must be clearly identified by position or durable marking to indicate the installation or circuit it isolates.

Where an installation is supplied from more than one source, a main switch is required for each source of supply or alternatively, a suitable interlock system must be provided.

WARNING
Before opening cover, isolation is required
at more than one location

Fig 5.22 Warning notice indicating that isolation is required from more than one position

Switching off for mechanical maintenance

Switching off to allow mechanical maintenance is not necessarily intended to provide protection from electric shock, but to allow non-electrical maintenance to be carried out without the risk of burns or injury from mechanical movement.

Selection and erection of equipment

An example of switching off for mechanical maintenance would be changing a lamp, or adjusting a drive belt on an electric motor. As access to live parts would not be available whilst carrying out such maintenance, isolation is not required. Prevention of the supply being unintentionally or inadvertently energised must be provided to ensure the operatives safety whilst carrying out the maintenance.

A switch used for mechanical maintenance need not have a facility to be locked off, providing it is local to the item of equipment, and under the control of the person carrying out the maintenance.

Emergency switching

Emergency switching is provided to remove, as quickly as possible, danger which may have occurred unexpectedly. It is also used to prevent danger where a dangerous situation may be about to happen and is prevented by operation of emergency switching.

This includes the emergency stopping of a machine or piece of electrical equipment.

An emergency switch may consist of either

- a single switching device directly cutting off the supply, *or*
- a combination of several items of equipment operated by a single action, removing the hazard by cutting off the supply.

A common example of the latter is a push button emergency stop connected in the control circuit of a contactor. Such devices must open upon de-energisation and be manually reset after the removal of the hazard.

Emergency switching devices should be readily accessible at places of danger, be readily identifiable and convenient for their intended use.

A plug and socket cannot be used as an emergency switch.

Functional switching

Functional switching is an operation intended to switch 'on' or 'off' or vary the supply of electrical energy to all or part of an installation for normal operating purposes. Examples of which are:

* a light switch
* a switch on a socket-outlet
* a switch used to switch a fan on or off

A functional switch must be provided for each part of a circuit that requires the function to be controlled independently of other parts of the installation. A single switch could however be used to operate several items of current-using equipment such as a row of luminaires for example. Such switches do not have to control all the live conductors but as a single-pole device it must be placed in the line conductor.

A plug and socket may be used as a functional switch providing the rating of the equipment is not more than 16 A.

Firefighter's Switches

A firefighter's switch is a device intended for use by the Fire Service to de-energise designated parts of the installation that operate at a voltage in excess of low voltage.

A firefighter's switch is required in low voltage circuits supplying:

* Exterior electrical installations operating at a voltage exceeding low voltage, *and*
* Interior discharge installations operating at a voltage exceeding low voltage.

Selection and erection of equipment

A covered market or shopping mall is considered to be an exterior installation, however a temporary installation indoors, typically used for exhibitions is considered as interior installation.

Common departures

1. A main linked switch or circuit-breaker as near as practicable to the origin of the installation has not been provided as a means of isolation
2. A means of isolation for the circuit has not been provided
3. Identification of the isolation device has been omitted
4. Incorrect device has been utilized for isolation, emergency switching or functional switching
5. Switch for mechanical maintenance does not prevent unintentional reclosure
6. Remote isolator has no provision to be secured in the open position
7. A readily accessible switch for a stationary appliance has not been provided

5.4   Earthing arrangements and Protective conductors

The protective measure, automatic disconnection of supply relies upon the earthing arrangement and protective conductors.

Generally the purposes of the earthing arrangements are:

- to provide a sufficiently low earth fault loop impedance for the required amount of fault current to circulate in the event of an earth fault, enabling disconnection of the circuit protective device in the required amount of time.
- to provide paths to earth of adequate current-carrying capacity so that protection of conductors and equipment against faults to earth can be provided.

Practically, the earthing arrangements are usually made up of the following:

- earthing conductor
- main earthing terminal

- main protective bonding conductor(s)
- supplementary bonding conductor(s)
- circuit protective conductor(s)

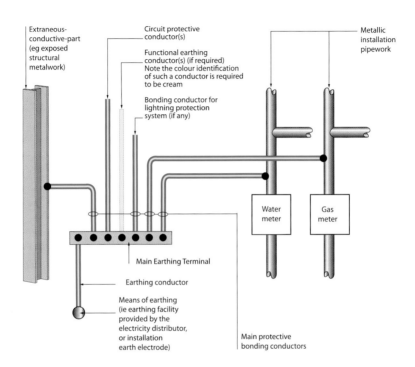

Extraneous-conductive-part (eg exposed structural metalwork)

Circuit protective conductor(s)

Functional earthing conductor(s) (if required) Note the colour identification of such a conductor is required to be cream

Bonding conductor for lightning protection system (if any)

Metallic installation pipework

Water meter

Gas meter

Main Earthing Terminal

Earthing conductor

Means of earthing (ie earthing facility provided by the electricity distributor, or installation earth electrode)

Main protective bonding conductors

5.23 Earthing arrangements

The main earthing terminal (MET) of an installation should be connected with Earth by one of the following:

Published by NICEIC. © Electrical Safety Council (Jan 2008)

Selection and erection of equipment

TN-S, to the earthed point of the source of energy.

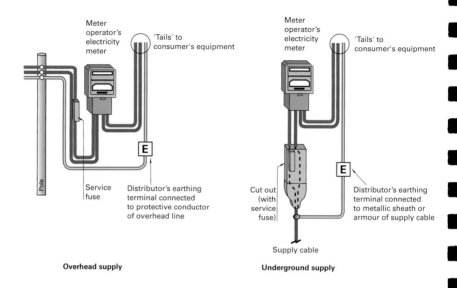

Fig 5.24 TN-S System

TN-C-S, where protective multiple earthing is provided, to the neutral of the source of supply.

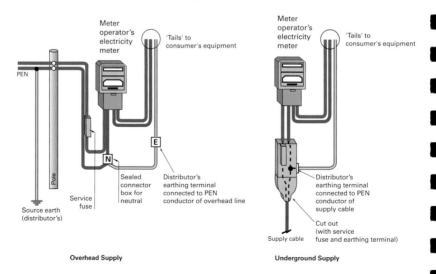

Fig 5.25 TN-C-S System

TT, via an earthing conductor to an earth electrode.

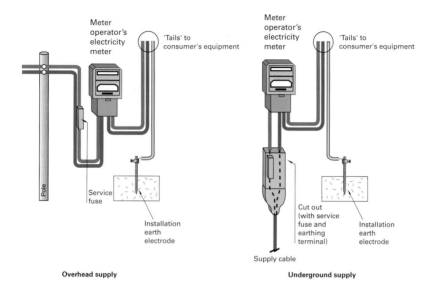

Fig 5.26 TT System

Earth electrodes

There are several earth electrodes recognised by *BS 7671* including tapes, wires, plates, structural steelwork etc. but the most common type is the earth rod. Such rods are generally of solid circular cross-section, and are made of copper, sometimes stainless or galvanised steel. They are produced in a number of standard lengths which can be connected together to provide a greater driven length.

BS 7671 does not allow the use of gas, water utility supply pipe or other services as an earth electrode.

Earthing conductor

The earthing conductor of an electrical installation connects the Main Earthing Terminal (MET) to the external earthing system.

Selection and erection of equipment

The conductor used for this purpose, the earthing conductor must meet the requirements of Section 543 and, where PME conditions apply, must also meet the requirements of Table 54.8 for the cross-sectional area of the conductor.

If the conductor is buried in the ground, then Table 54.1 provides the minimum cross-sectional area that may be used.

Main earthing terminal (MET)

A Main Earthing Terminal (MET) is required in every installation for connection to the means of earthing and the installation protective conductors (listed below):

- Circuit protective conductors, *and*
- The protective bonding conductors, *and*
- Functional earthing conductors (if required), *and*
- Lightning protection system bonding conductor (if any).

Circuit protective conductors, protective bonding conductors, functional earthing conductors (if required) and lightning protection system bonding conductor (if any).

Bolted link

Earthing conductor

Means of earthing

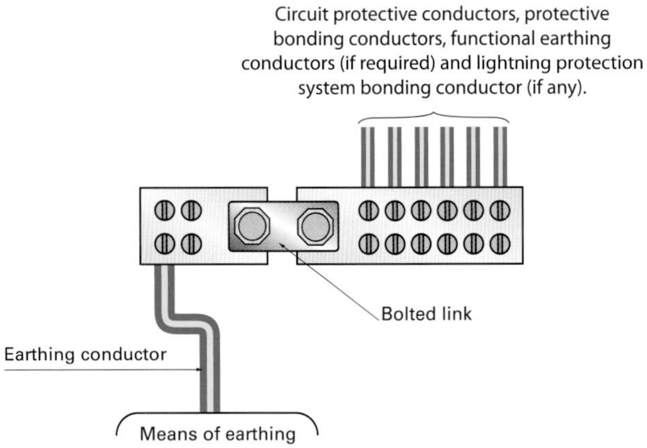

Fig 5.27 MET with disconnecting link

To facilitate measurement of the resistance of the earthing arrangements a means of disconnecting the installation earthing conductor will be required. This provision may be combined with the main earthing terminal as shown above.

Cross-sectional area of protective conductors.

The cross-sectional area of the protective conductor should be either:

- Calculated in accordance with Regulation 543.1.3 or

- Selected in accordance with Regulation 543.1.4

The simplest method which avoids calculation is by 'selection' in accordance with Regulation 543.1.4. It may however result in a larger cable than is necessary.

If the protective conductor:

- is not an integral part of a cable, *or*
- is not formed by conduit, trunking or ducting, *or*
- is not contained in an enclosure formed by a wiring system,

the cross-sectional area should not be less than 2.5 mm^2 copper equivalent, if protected from mechanical damage, and 4 mm^2 copper equivalent if mechanical protection is provided.

Where the csa of a protective conductor is to be selected, Table 54.7 should be consulted. This table provides the minimum cross-sectional area of the protective conductor in relation to the csa of the associated line conductor.

Selection and erection of equipment

Table 54.7 Minimum cross-sectional area of protective conductor in relation to the cross-sectional area of associated line conductor

Cross-sectional area of line conductor S	Minimum cross-sectional area of the corresponding protective conductor	
	If the protective conductor is of the same material as the line conductor	If the protective conductor is not the same material as the line conductor
$S \leq 16$	S	$\dfrac{k_1}{k_2} \times S$
$16 < S \leq 35$	16	$\dfrac{k_1}{k_2} \times 16$
$S > 35$	$\dfrac{S}{2}$	$\dfrac{k_1}{k_2} \times \dfrac{S}{2}$

Where

k_1   is the value of k for the line conductor, selected from Table 43.1 in Chapter 43 according to the materials of both conductor and insulation.

k_2   is the value of k for the protective conductor, selected from Tables 54.2, 54.3, 54.4, 54.5 or 54.6, as applicable.

Calculation of protective conductor size (adiabatic equation) If the 'selection' method is not adopted, then the cross-sectional area of the protective conductor must be calculated using the following formula:

$$S = \frac{\sqrt{I^2 t}}{k} \qquad \textbf{This is called the adiabatic equation}$$

Where,

S - is the nominal cross-sectional area of the conductor in mm^2

I - is the value in amperes (rms for a.c.) of the fault current for a fault of negligible impedance, which can flow through the associated protective device.

t - is the operating time of the disconnecting device in seconds corresponding to the fault current I in amperes

k - is a factor taking account of the resistivity, temperature coefficient and heat capacity of the conductor material, and the appropriate initial and final temperatures of the conductors. (Tables 54.2 to 52.6 provide values of K for a range of cables and conductor types).

The adiabatic equation is based on the assumption that the duration of the earth fault current is so short that none of the heat energy produced in the protective conductor escapes before the protective device operates. This assumption is never true, but is reasonably accurate providing the operating time of the disconnecting device does not exceed 5 s, as is normally required by *BS 7671*.

Example: Calculate the minimum csa for a circuit protective conductor for a circuit protected by a 40 A *BS 88* fuse (assume maximum Z s and 5 s disconnection time). The cable is 70 $^{\circ}$C thermoplastic single insulated with copper conductors, bunched with cables. The nominal voltage is 230 V.

$$S = \frac{\sqrt{I^2 t}}{k}$$

I (current) = 230/1.35 = 170 A.

t (disconnection time) for a 40 A *BS 88* fuse with 170 A flowing is 5 seconds (check Appendix 3 Table 3.3B).

k (from Table 54.3) 115 (cable assumed to be less than 300 mm^2, with a 40 A device).

$$\therefore S \; \frac{\sqrt{28900 \times 5}}{k} = \frac{380}{115} = 3.3 \text{ mm}^2.$$

A 4 mm^2 cable will be required.

Published by NICEIC. © Electrical Safety Council (Jan 2008)

Selection and erection of equipment

A protective conductor may consist of one or more of the following:

- a single-core cable coloured green-and-yellow
- a conductor in a cable
- a bonding conductor
- a metal sheath, screen or armouring of a cable
- a metal conduit, trunking or other enclosure which is electrically continuous
- an extraneous-conductive-part complying with Regulation 543.2.6.

Metal utility supply pipes and metal flexible conduit must not be used as protective conductors. Extraneous-conductive-parts may be used as a protective conductor provided the requirements of 543.2.6. are met.

Where the conduit, trunking or the sheath/armour of a cable is used as a protective conductor, the earthing terminal at each accessory must be connected by a separate protective conductor to the earthing terminal in the accessory box.

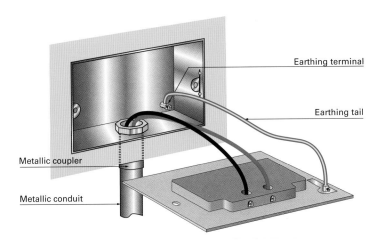

Fig 5.28 A protective conductor connecting accessory to box

Earthing requirements for the installation of equipment having high protective conductor currents.

a. General

When energized and in normal use, some electrical equipment can cause current to flow in the circuit protective conductors. This process is referred to as functional earthing as the equipment concerned requires the current to flow in the protective conductor to function or operate normally. Such 'protective conductor current' is often associated with filters and suppressors in items such as computers, and telecommunications equipment.

Any equipment or circuits having a protective conductor current greater than 3.5 mA may increase the risk of electric shock. There are therefore, additional requirements stipulated for these circuits.

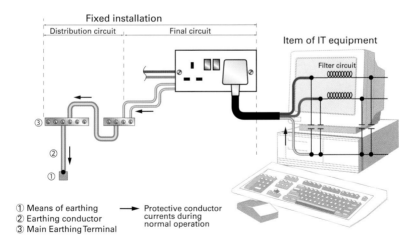

① Means of earthing
② Earthing conductor
③ Main Earthing Terminal

➤ Protective conductor currents during normal operation

Fig 5.29 Typical equipment and circuit arrangement illustrating high protective conductor currents

Published by NICEIC. © Electrical Safety Council (Jan 2008)

Selection and erection of equipment

Equipment which in normal service, will have a protective
conductor current exceeding 3.5 mA, but less than 10 mA
must be either:

- permanently connected to the fixed wiring of the
  installation without the use of a plug and socket-outlet, *or*
- connected by means of a connector complying with *BS
  EN 60309-2* (that is, an industrial-type connector as
  shown below).

Fig 5.30 Connector complying with *BS EN 60309-2*

c. Equipment having a protective conductor current
exceeding 10 mA, and circuits where the total
protective conductor current exceeds 10 mA

Where an item of equipment having a protective conductor
current exceeding 10 mA is to be supplied, there are
several requirements and these can be met in a number of
different ways. The following aspects of the installation
must be considered:

- the means of connection of the equipment.
- the final circuits and distribution circuits supplying
  the equipment.
- the termination of protective conductors.

Equipment with a protective conductor current exceeding 10 mA should be permanently connected to the fixed wiring of the installation, the protective conductor being selected in accordance with Regulation 543.7.1.3.

Where a plug and socket-outlet arrangement is used they must comply with *BS EN 60309-2*. In addition, one of the following requirements must be met:

- the csa of the associated flexible cable should not be less than 2.5 mm^2 for plugs rated at 16 A and not less than 4 mm^2 for plugs rated above 16 A *or*,
- the protective conductor of the associated flexible cable should have a csa not less than the line conductor.

d. Final circuits and distribution circuits where the total protective conductor current is liable to exceed 10 mA.

Every final circuit and distribution circuit intended to supply an item (or items) of equipment, where the total protective conductor current is likely to exceed 10 mA, must meet requirements of a high integrity protective connection. Five options are provided in Regulation 543.7.1.3; the following text provides a brief overview of the options:

- A single protective conductor having a csa of not less than 10 mm^2.
- A single copper protective conductor having a csa of not less than 4 mm^2, the protective conductor being enclosed to provide additional mechanical protection.
- Two individual protective conductors, each one complying with the requirements of Section 543. It is permitted for the two protective conductors to be of different types (for further information see 543.7.1.3 (iii)).
- An earth monitoring system to *BS 4444* configured to automatically disconnect the supply to the equipment in the event of a continuity fault in the protective conductor.

Selection and erection of equipment

- A double-wound transformer or equivalent in which the input and output circuits are electrically separate (for further information see Regulation 543.7.1.3 (v)).

e. Socket-outlet final circuits

A final circuit supplying socket-outlets or connection units where it is known or reasonably to be expected that the total protective conductor current in normal service will exceed 10 mA, must comply with Regulation Group 543.7.2. Where this is the case, the final circuit must be provided with high integrity protective conductor connections, such as two individual protective conductors or a single protective conductor having a csa of not less than 10 mm^2.

Where two separate protective conductors are used, Regulation 543.7.1.4 requires the socket-outlets and other accessories in the circuit to have two separate earth terminals (as shown in Fig 54.10 below), to enable the ends of the protective conductors to be terminated independently of each other at all connection points.

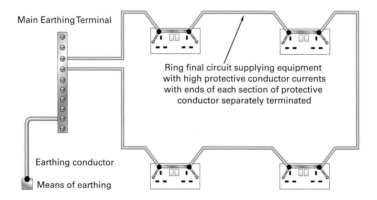

Main Earthing Terminal

Ring final circuit supplying equipment with high protective conductor currents with ends of each section of protective conductor separately terminated

Earthing conductor

Means of earthing

Fig 5.31 Separate protective conductor connections at all connection points

A ring final circuit, by its particular configuration, provides duplication of the protective conductor and, provided the requirements of Section 543 of *BS 7671* are met, a high integrity protective conductor connection exists. Where a cable branch (spur) is provided, this requires a high integrity protective conductor connection and separate termination of the protective conductors as described.

Where a radial final circuit is utilized it must be provided with a high integrity protective conductor connection. Where duplicate protective conductors are employed, separate termination of the protective conductor ends is required. The duplicate protective conductor can be provided by any of the following options:

a) the protective conductor being connected as a ring, *or*

b) a separate protective conductor being provided at the final socket-outlet by connection to metal conduit or ducting, *or*

c) the protective conductor of an adjacent radial circuit can also be employed (providing certain requirements are met).

Where any of the above situations exist, the protective conductor connection arrangements at the distribution board will, in many cases, be affected. For example, there will in some cases be duplicate protective conductors separately terminated. This may require the installation of an additional facility for the termination of protective conductors. Distribution equipment manufacturers' provide such facilities for their equipment. At the distribution board information should be provided indicating those circuits having a high protective conductor current, and such information must be so positioned as to be visible to a person modifying or extending the circuit.

Selection and erection of equipment

The overriding purpose of main protective bonding is to reduce the prospective shock voltage and is part of the protective measure Automatic Disconnection of Supply (ADS). Most electrical installations require this bonding to be carried out.

It should be remembered that where an existing installation is to have alterations or additions carried out, the main protective bonding will have to be installed to the requirements of *BS 7671* Chapter 54 as part of the alteration or addition. **This is often overlooked.**

Protective bonding conductors complying with Chapter 54 should connect to the protective earthing terminal, extraneous-conductive-parts including the following:

- water installation pipes
- gas installation pipes
- other installation pipework and ducting
- central heating and air conditioning systems
- exposed structural steelwork

In addition to the above, connection of a lightning protection system to protective equipotential bonding should be made in accordance with *BS EN 62305*

There is an increased use of plastic pipework utilised for the gas and water services, and generally if the incoming service pipes are plastic, there is no need for them to be bonded.

Cross-sectional area of main bonding conductors

Where PME conditions do not apply, a main protective bonding conductor should have a csa of not less than half that required for the earthing conductor of the installation and not less than 6 mm^2.

The bonding conductor in the above case need not exceed 25 mm^2 if made of copper, or if other material have a csa affording equivalent conductance.

Where PME conditions apply, the main protective bonding conductor(s) should be selected in accordance with the neutral conductor of the incoming supply and by the use of Table 54.8 reproduced below.

Minimum cross-sectional area of the main protective bonding conductor in relation to the neutral of the supply

Copper equivalent cross-sectional area of the supply neutral conductor	Minimum copper equivalent cross-sectional area of the main protective bonding conductor
35 mm^2 or less	10 mm^2
over 35 mm^2 up to 50 mm^2	16 mm^2
over 50 mm^2 up to 95 mm^2	25 mm^2
over 95 mm^2 up to 150 mm^2	35 mm^2
over 150 mm^2	50 mm^2

It should be noted that the sizes of earthing conductor, main protective bonding conductors and supplementary bonding conductors may be specified as a larger csa. Such specifications may be the requirements of a local authority or by the designer of the electrical installation, in which case they must be adhered to.

The main bonding connections to any gas, water or other service must be made as near as is practicable to the point of entry into the building. Where there is an insulating section or meter, then the connection should be made on the consumer's metal pipework, within 600 mm of the meter. If the meter is located externally, then the connection should be made at the point of entry of the service to the building.

Selection and erection of equipment

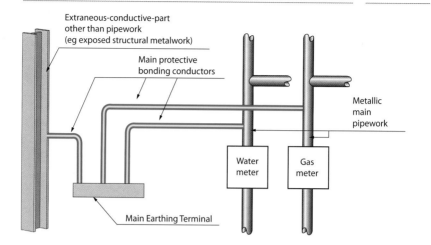

Fig 5.32 Main protective bonding conductors

Main protective bonding connections to metal pipework should normally be made using bonding clamps complying with *BS 951*: Specification for clamps for earthing and bonding purposes. Clamps should be selected to suit both the pipe diameter and bonding conductor size.

Other suitable means of connection may be required when connecting to extraneous-conductive-parts other than pipes, such as structural steelwork.

The clamp selected must be suitable for the environmental conditions at the point of connection. This is typically identified by the colour of the clamp body or a coloured stripe on the warning label.

Fig 5.33 BS 951 clamp

Fig 5.34 Clamps for different environmental conditions.

A red stripe on the label indicates it is only suitable where conditions are non-corrosive, clean and dry (e.g. hot pipes indoors). A blue or green stripe on the label indicates that the clamp is suitable for all (including corrosive and humid) conditions.

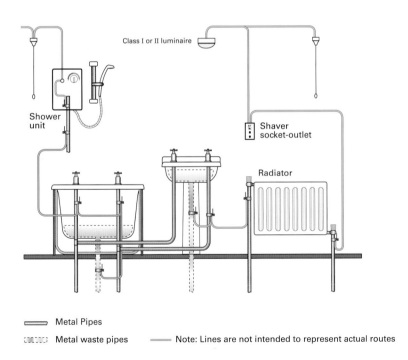

Class I or II luminaire

Shower unit

Shaver socket-outlet

Radiator

━━━ Metal Pipes

┈┈┈ Metal waste pipes ━━━ Note: Lines are not intended to represent actual routes

Fig 5.35 Typical supplementary bonding connections

Selection and erection of equipment

(i). Introduction

Supplementary bonding is an additional protective provision that is used to enhance the standard fault protection systems as outlined in Chapter 41. It may be required where disconnection times cannot be met or where required due to the special nature of the installation. Part 7 of the Regulations gives further details on the requirements of supplementary bonding in certain special installations or locations.

Supplementary bonding involves connecting together the conductive parts of all electrical items and non-electrical items, to prevent the occurrence of a dangerous voltage between them under earth fault conditions.

Supplementary bonding should be provided by either a separate supplementary conductor, a conductive part of a permanent and reliable nature (including a circuit protective conductor or an extraneous-conductive-part) or a combination of both. Where doubt exists in relation to the effectiveness of supplementary bonding an assessment should be made by using the calculation contained within Regulation 415.2.2

The exception to the above requirement for supplementary bonding is where a fixed appliance is connected by a short length of flexible cord from an adjacent connection unit or other accessory, in which case the protective conductor also provides the function of a supplementary bonding conductor for the short section. A typical example of this is a heated towel rail within a bathroom.

Fig 5.36 Picture of heated towel rail

Supplementary bonding conductor sizing

The table below sets out the basic requirements of Regulations 544.2.1, 544.2.2 & 544.2.3 relating to the size of supplementary bonding conductors:

Table 544.1 Minimum csa of copper conductors required for supplementary bonding.

Regulations	Bonding conductor connecting			
	Sheathed or mechanically protected	Two exposed-conductive-parts	An exposed-conductive-part and an extraneous-conductive-parts	Two extraneous-conductive-parts
544.2.1, 544.2.2 & 544.2.3	Yes	CSA ≥ CSA of smaller cpc	CSA ≥ CSA of cpc	CSA ≥ 2.5 mm^2
	No	CSA ≥ 4.0 mm^2	CSA ≥ 4.0 mm^2	CSA ≥ 4.0 mm^2

Selection and erection of equipment

Common departures

1. Main protective bonding conductors have been omitted
2. Main bonding conductor is undersized
3. Main bonding conductor termination is not near the point of entry into premises
4. Supplementary bonding is of insufficient cross-sectional area
5. A socket circuit forming part of a TT installation not RCD protected
6. A socket-outlet with a current rating not exceeding 20 A which can be used by ordinary persons and intended for general use is not protected by a 30 mA RCD
7. Mobile equipment for use outdoors with a current rating not exceeding 32A is not protected by an RCD

Part 6
Inspection and Testing

6.0   Introduction

Every new electrical installation, and every alteration and
addition must be thoroughly inspected and tested
(Regulation 610.1) and any defects made good before the
installation is put into service. Or, in the case of alterations
and additions, before the electrical installation is put back
into service.

Precautions should be taken to avoid danger to persons
and damage to property and installed equipment during
inspection and testing. This applies to both the inspection
process and the testing of the electrical installation.
Persons carrying out the inspection and testing must
comply with the relevant requirements of the Electricity at
Work Regulations, in particular Regulation 14, 'working on
or near live conductors' and to the associated guidance
provided in the Memorandum of guidance on the Electricity
at Work Regulations.

Even the most experienced electricians can make mistakes
and the process of inspection and testing will help identify
any mistakes, which can then be corrected before the
installation is put into service.

In addition to this, by thoroughly inspecting and testing the
electrical installation, a record is provided of the condition of
the installation work carried out. This provides documentary
evidence for the persons responsible for the safety of the
installations (including owners and users) that in the opinion
of the competent persons, the electrical installation has
been installed to a satisfactory standard of safety.

The provision of certification on completion of the
verification, is a requirement of Regulation 610.6

The verification of the electrical installation should include
comparison of the results with the relevant criteria, to confirm
that the requirements of the regulations have been met.

For a detailed look at the requirements of Part 6 of *BS 7671*, and for guidance about how to carry out the process, refer to the NICEIC publications, 'Inspection, Testing and Certification' and 'Domestic Periodic Inspection, Testing and Reporting'.

Persons who do not consider themselves competent, to carry out inspection, testing and certification should complete an appropriate training course and assessment provided by a reputable training organisation, such as NICEIC Training.

Part 6 of *BS 7671* includes three chapters:

Chapter 61 Initial verification
Chapter 62 Periodic inspection and testing
Chapter 63 Certification and reporting

6.1 Initial verification

6.1.1 Inspection

The inspection shall precede testing and is normally done with that part of the installation under inspection disconnected from the supply.

Regulation 611.2 requires that the inspection be made to verify that the installed equipment is:

- in compliance with Section 511 (compliance with standards, for example, British Standards)
- correctly selected and erected in accordance with the Regulations
- not visibly damaged or defective so as to impair safety

The inspection process includes checking of the items relevant to the installation and where necessary during erection.

The items for inspection are detailed on the model forms within *BS 7671* for 'schedule of inspections' as shown below.

Inspection of the electrical installation should be carried out thoroughly and diligently and not considered as just a tick list. Each section should be addressed and assessed separately for compliance with the requirements by the competent persons involved.

SCHEDULE OF ITEMS INSPECTED   † See note below

METHODS OF PROTECTION AGAINST ELECTRIC SHOCK

Basic and fault protection

Extra low voltage
- SELV
- PELV

Double or reinforced insulation
- Double or Reinforced Insulation

Basic protection
- Insulation of live parts
- Obstacles **
- Barriers or enclosures
- Placing out of reach **

Fault protection

Automatic disconnection of supply
- Presence of earthing conductor
- Presence of circuit protective conductors
- Presence of main equipotential bonding conductors
- Presence of earthing arrangements for combined protective and functional purposes
- Presence of adequate arrangements for alternative source(s), where applicable
- FELV
- Choice and setting of protective and monitoring devices (for fault protection and/or overcurrent protection)

Non-conducting location **
- Absence of protective conductors

Earth-free equipotential bonding **
- Presence of earth-free equipotential bonding

Electrical separation
- For **one** item of current using equipment
- For **more** than one item of current using equipment **

Additional protection
- Presence of residual current device(s)
- Presence of supplementary bonding conductors

* For use in controlled supervised/conditions only

Prevention of mutual detrimental influence
- Proximity of non-electrical services and other influences
- Segregation of Band I and Band II circuits or Band II insulation used
- Segregation of Safety Circuits

Identification
- Presence of diagrams, instructions, circuit charts and similar information
- Presence of danger notices and other warning notices
- Labelling of protective devices, switches and terminals
- Identification of conductors

Cables and Conductors
- Selection of conductors for current carrying capacity and voltage drop
- Erection methods
- Routing of cables in prescribed zones
- Cables incorporating earthed armour or sheath or run in an earthed wiring system, or otherwise protected against nails, screws and the like
- Additional protection by 30mA RCD for cables concealed in walls (where required, in premises not under the supervision of skilled or instructed persons)
- Connection of conductors
- Presence of fire barriers, suitable seals and protection against thermal effects

General
- Presence and correct location of appropriate devices for isolation and switching
- Adequacy of access to switchgear and other equipment
- Particular protective measures for special installations and locations
- Connection of single-pole devices for protection or switching in line conductors only
- Correct connection of accessories and equipment
- Presence of undervoltage protective devices
- Selection of equipment and protective measures appropriate to external influences
- Selection of appropriate functional switching devices

SCHEDULE OF ITEMS TESTED   † See note below
- External earth fault loop impedance, Z_e
- Installation earth electrode resistance, R_A
- Continuity of protective conductors
- Continuity of ring final circuit conductors
- Insulation resistance between live conductors
- Insulation resistance between live conductors and Earth
- Protection by separation of circuits
- Basic protection by barrier or enclosure provided during erection
- Insulation of non-conducting floors or walls
- Polarity
- Earth fault loop impedance, Z_s
- Verification of phase sequence
- Operation of residual current devices
- Functional testing of assemblies
- Verification of voltage drop

SCHEDULE OF ADDITIONAL RECORDS* (See attached schedule)
Page No(s)

Note: Additional page(s) must be identified by the Electrical Installation Certificate serial number and page number(s).

All boxes must be completed. '✓' indicates that an inspection or a test was carried out and that the result was **satisfactory**. 'N/A' indicates that an inspection or test was **not applicable** to the particular installation.

Where the electrical work to which this certificate relates includes the installation of a fire alarm system and/or an emergency lighting system (or a part of such systems), this electrical safety certificate should be accompanied by the particular certificate(s) for the system(s).

This form is based on the model shown in Appendix 6 of BS 7671: 2008.
Copyright The Electrical Safety Council (Jan 2008).

Page 3 of [   ]

Page of [   ]

ICMA/5

Original (To the person ordering)

Fig 6.1 Inspection schedule

6.1.2 Testing

The tests of Regulations 612.2 to 612.13, where relevant, shall be carried out and the results compared with the relevant criteria. The measuring instruments, monitoring equipment and methods shall be chosen in accordance with the relevant parts of *BS EN 61557* which provides the requirement for electrical safety in low voltage distribution systems and equipment for electrical testing and monitoring.

The relevant tests should be carried out in the order shown before the installation is energized. If any test indicates a failure to comply that test and any preceding tests, shall be repeated after the fault has been rectified. The order of tests for a periodic inspection and test may vary from those listed.

Detailed description of the methods and order of tests are provided in the NICEIC publications 'Inspection, Testing and Certification' and 'Domestic Periodic Inspection, Testing and Reporting'.

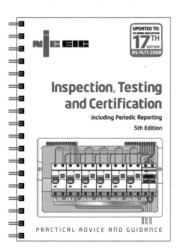
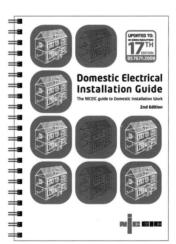

The order of tests to be carried out on a new installation is:

1. Continuity of protective conductors, including main and supplementary equipotential bonding

2. Continuity of ring final circuit conductors
3. Insulation resistance
4. Protection by separation of circuits
5. Insulation resistance / impedance of floors and walls
6. Polarity
7. Earth electrode resistance
8. Earth fault loop impedance
9. Additional protection
10. Prospective fault current
11. Check of phase sequence
12. Functional testing
13. Verification of voltage drop

6.1.3 Continuity of protective conductors

Testing the continuity of protective conductors includes earthing conductors, main protective and supplementary bonding conductors and circuit protective conductors.

(It is recommended that the test is carried out with a supply having a no-load voltage between 4 V and 24 V, d.c. or a.c. and a short-circuit current of not less than 200 mA)

Using a low resistance ohmmeter, typically capable of reading a range 0 to 2 ohm with a resolution of at least 0.01 ohm for digital instruments, a check is made that the protective conductors are connected to each required point in the installation and throughout the circuit(s). The test values should be compared with relevant criteria.

When testing continuity of protective conductors, it is important to identify whether parallel paths are being measured as opposed to the conductor resistance. Therefore the disconnection of one end of the conductor may be necessary.

On distribution and final circuits, after isolating the main switch (using a safe isolation procedure) this test may be carried out by measuring the circuit protective conductor only, with a long wander lead (R_2), or by using a temporary link between the circuit protective conductor and the line conductor and measuring between the two. ($R_1 + R_2$).

Where a switch is installed in the circuit, this should be operated in order to verify polarity.

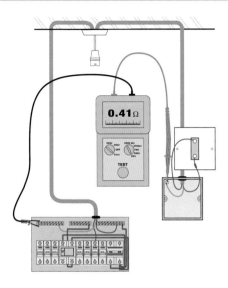

Fig 6.2 Continuity of protective conductors

6.1.4 Continuity of ring final circuit conductors

A three-step test is required to verify the continuity of the line, neutral and circuit protective conductor (cpc).

Step 1:

The end-to-end resistance of each of the line, neutral and circuit protective conductors is measured separately, resulting in values for r_1, r_n and r_2 respectively. The resistance values obtained should typically be within 0.05 ohms if the conductors are the same cross-sectional-area. If as is quite common, the cpc is of a smaller csa than the line and neutral conductors, then the resistance of the cpc will be proportionally higher.

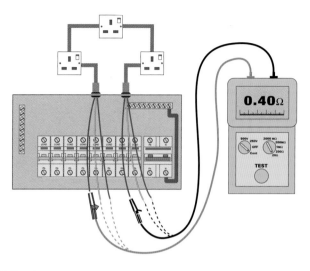

Fig 6.3 Step 1

Step 2:

The line and neutral conductors are connected together so that the outgoing line conductor is connected to the returning neutral conductor and vice-versa. The resistance between line and neutral is measured at each socket-outlet.

The readings obtained at each outlet connected directly to the ring, should be the same. The value should equate to approximately one quarter of the resistance of the line plus the neutral loop resistances. $(r_1 + r_n) / 4$

Any socket-outlets wired as spurs will give a higher reading due to the resistance of the spur conductors.

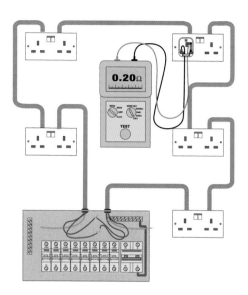

Fig 6.4 Step 2

Step 3:

The above step is then repeated but with the line and cpc cross-connected. The resistance between line and cpc is measured at each outlet and the value obtained should equate to approximately one quarter of the resistance of the line plus the cpc loop resistances $(r_1 + r_2) / 4$

Any socket-outlets wired as spurs will give a higher reading due to the resistance of the spur conductors. If incorrect interconnection in the ring circuit (bridges) have been installed, the resistance readings at some socket-outlets will be inconsistent with readings at other socket-outlets.

Measurement of resistance at socket-outlets may be made by plugging in a suitable socket-outlet/continuity test instrument lead interface adapter, such as that obtained from NICEIC Direct.

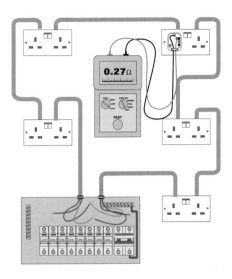

Fig 6.5 Step 3

The highest value measured represents the maximum $(R_1 + R_2)$ for the circuit and should be recorded on the schedule of test results. This value can be used to determine the earth fault loop impedance of the circuit and to verify compliance with the Regulations.

This sequence of tests also verifies the polarity of each socket-outlet.

6.1.5 Insulation resistance

The insulation resistance test is carried out to verify compliance with *BS 7671*, Table 61; that the insulation of conductors, accessories and equipment is satisfactory and that conductors are not short-circuited or have defective insulation.

Before testing it is important to:

- remove all current-using equipment including lamps, pilot lamps etc from the circuit(s) to avoid inaccurate test readings

- if a measurement between live conductors is being carried out then any voltage sensitive equipment should be disconnected to avoid being damaged by the test voltage
- check that there is no electrical connection between line or neutral conductors and earth.

Where it is not possible to disconnect equipment connected between live conductors, (for example, when carrying out periodic inspection and testing) a temporary link may be installed between live conductors (when measuring insulation resistance between live conductors and Earth).

On a 230 V / 400 V installation, the test is carried out using an insulation resistance tester at a test voltage of 500 V d.c. as shown below, and should exceed the minimum value of 1 Megohm given in Table 61 of *BS 7671*.

However if there is sensitive equipment connected between the live and protective conductors (for example, a surge protective device) that cannot be disconnected, then the test voltage may be reduced to 250 V d.c.

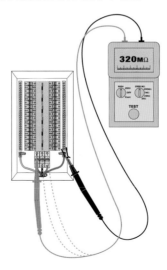

Fig 6.6 Insulation resistance measurement between one of the line conductors and neutral for a three-phase distribution board with its final circuits connected.

Where insulation tests are carried out in installations that incorporate SELV or PELV or electrical separation, the Regulation group 612.4 should be followed.

6.1.6   Polarity

The polarity of all circuits must be verified before connection to the supply. For radial circuits, the $(R_1 + R_2)$ method described in the 'continuity of protective conductors' should be made at each point. For ring circuits, the method described previously will verify correct polarity.

After connection of the supply, polarity should be confirmed by using an approved voltage indicator.

For the testing methods refer to the NICEIC book on 'Inspection, testing and certification' or 'Domestic Periodic Inspection, Testing and Reporting' as appropriate.

6.1.7   Earth electrode resistance

A measurement must be taken of the earth electrode resistance to earth which can be done by using either:

• an earth electrode resistance test instrument, *or*
• an earth fault loop impedance test instrument.

For the testing methods, refer to the NICEIC book on 'Inspection, testing and certification' or Domestic Periodic Inspection, Testing and Reporting' as appropriate.

If an earth fault loop impedance tester is used it should be connected between the line conductor at the source of supply of the TT installation, and the earth electrode and a test performed using a suitable safe system of work.

The impedance reading taken is treated as the earth electrode resistance.

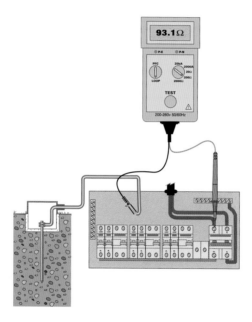

Fig 6.7 Measurement of earth fault loop impendance

The earth electrode resistance must meet the requirements of Regulation 411.5.3.

6.1.8 Earth fault loop impedance

If automatic disconnection of supply is used as a protective measure, then a test for earth fault loop impedance must be carried out in order to check compliance with the requirements of Section 411.

The earth fault loop impedance external to the installation
is measured by connecting the loop impedance tester to
the supply line conductor and the supply earth. It is very
important that the supply earth is disconnected to prevent
the measurement of any parallel paths that may exist.
**Before this test is carried out it is necessary to check
that the installation is switched off.**

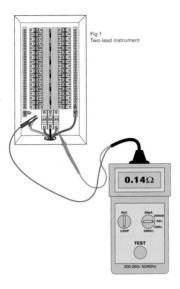

Fig 1
Two-lead instrument

Fig 6.8 Measurement of external loop impedance (Z_e)

To measure the earth fault loop impedance of a final circuit,
one of two methods may be employed:

- to make a direct reading between the line terminal and
  the circuit protective conductor terminal at the furthest
  point of the circuit (Z_s). This is the normal method for
  testing socket-outlets.
- to use the previously recorded value of ($R_1 + R_2$),
  obtained during the continuity testing, and add this to
  a measured value of external loop impedance (Z_e), to
  obtain the circuit earth fault loop impedance (Z_s)

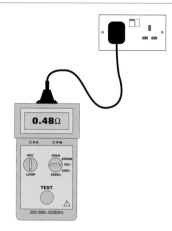

Fig 6.9 Measurement of earth fault loop impedance

For the testing methods refer to the NICEIC book on 'Inspection, testing and certification' or 'Domestic Periodic Inspection, Testing and Reporting', as appropriate.

6.1.9 Additional protection

Where fault protection and/or additional protection is to be provided by an RCD, the effectiveness of automatic disconnection of supply by the RCDs should be verified.

6.1.10 Prospective fault current

Prospective fault current is the maximum fault current that is likely to occur in the installation. The design and selection of equipment is based upon knowledge of this value. The prospective fault current should be verified at the origin and at other relevant points of the installation.

This may be carried out by either:

- enquiry
- measurement
- calculation

Protective devices and switchgear must be able to withstand the prospective fault current available at their point in the installation. Measurement at the origin and the other relevant points where protective devices are required to operate under fault conditions will verify this. The breaking capacity of each protective device should not be less than the prospective fault current at its point of installation.

For single-phase installations, two measurements are taken:

- prospective short circuit current measured between line and neutral, *and*
- prospective earth fault current measured between line and earth

Single-phase prospective fault current is taken as the larger of the two values.

For three-phase installations, the maximum prospective fault current is likely to be between line conductors. As an approximation, which errs on the side of safety, the prospective fault current line to line can be taken as twice the prospective fault current measured between one line and neutral. This value should be recorded in the appropriate section on the Certificate.

For the testing methods refer to the NICEIC book on 'Inspection, testing and certification' or 'Domestic Periodic Inspection, Testing and Reporting', as appropriate.

6.1.11 Check of phase sequence

For multi-phase circuits, it should be verified that the phase sequence is maintained.

6.1.12 Functional testing

The effectiveness of any test facility incorporated in RCDs should be verified.

Assemblies such as switchgear, control gear, interlocks and controls should be subjected to a functional test to confirm that they are properly mounted, adjusted and installed in accordance with the requirements of the Regulations.

6.2 Periodic inspection and testing

The completion of a Periodic Inspection Report may be required to report on any factors impairing the safety of an electrical installation.

NICEIC experience indicates that persons undertaking periodic inspection reporting need to have above-average knowledge and experience of electrical installation matters, to enable them to safely and accurately assess the condition of a existing electrical installation.

6.3 Certification and Reporting

Upon completion of the initial verification of a new installation or alterations / additions to an existing installation, an Electrical Installation Certificate must be provided. It should include details of the extent of the installation covered by the Certificate, together with a record of the inspection and a schedule of test results.

Person(s) responsible for the design, construction and the inspection and testing should sign the Certificate which takes account of their respective responsibilities and the Certificate should be given to the person ordering the work.

If the work completed is of a minor nature, for example not a new circuit, then a Minor Electrical Installation Works Certificate can be completed. Any defects found on the existing installation should be recorded on the Certificate.

For information on Certification and Reporting refer to the NICEIC book on 'Inspection, testing and certification' and/or *'Domestic Periodic Inspection, Testing and Reporting'*, as appropriate.

Part 7
Special installations and locations

7.0   Intoduction

Part 7 of *BS 7671* contains Regulations relating to special installations or locations. All of the installations or locations can be seen as areas of increased risk from electric shock, and possibly fire. For this reason they require special consideration in terms of the design and construction of their electrical installations.

Part 7 contains additional Regulations that supplement or modify the general requirements in other parts of the Regulations.

There are now 14 special installations or locations in *BS 7671 : 2008* (17th Edition) many of which are outside the scope of this Guide, however it is worth identifying the complete list of the contents of Part 7.

Section in BS7671	Title of special installation or location
701	Locations containing a bath or shower
702	Swimming pools and other basins
703	Rooms and cabins containing sauna heaters
704	Construction and demolition site installations
705	Agricultural and horticultural premises
706	Conducting locations with restrictive movement
708	Electrical installations in caravan/camping parks and similar locations
709	Marinas and similar locations
711	Exhibitions, shows and stands
712	Solar photovoltaic (pv) power supply systems
717	Mobile or transportable units
721	Electrical installations in caravans and motor caravans
740	Temporary electrical installations for structures, amusement devices and booths at fairgrounds, amusement parks and circuses
753	Floor and ceiling heating systems

7.1 Locations containing a bath or shower

A location containing a bath or shower is considered to be a location where there is increased risk of electric shock due to:

- a reduction in body resistance caused by either immersion or by wet skin
- likely contact of substantial areas of the body with earth potential

The room containing the bath or shower is 'zoned' and the zones used to specify in relation to which protective measures, switchgear, control gear, accessories and current using equipment can be used in each of the prescribed zones.

To fully understand the zonal concept it is important to refer to the diagrams shown below.

ZONE 0 is: the interior of the bath tub or shower basin

Note: *for showers without a basin, the height of zone 0 is 0.10 m extending to the same horizontal extent as Zone 1.*

ZONE 1 is:

(i) the three dimensional space immediately above the bath or shower basin up to a height of 2.25 m. For showers without a basin and for showers without a basin, but with a fixed partition, there are specific dimensions (see the diagrams below).

(ii) the space under the bath or shower, unless it is only accessible by a key or a tool in which case it is considered to be outside the zones (see Fig 701.8 for an example).

(iii) the vertical surface at a distance 1.20 m from the centre point of the fixed water outlet on the wall or ceiling for showers without a basin

ZONE 2 is: <u>the area that extends to a point horizontally 0.6 m starting from the border of zone 1. Zone 2 extends 2.25 m vertically from finished floor level (or to the highest fixed shower head or water outlet, whichever is the higher)</u>

Note: *for showers without a basin there is no Zone 2 but Zone 1 is extended horizontally a further 0.6 m.*

The following diagrams taken from BS 7671 illustrate the zone dimensions relating to a location containing a bath. For the zonal dimensions of a location containing a shower, refer to Fig 701.1 and Fig 701.2 of BS 7671.

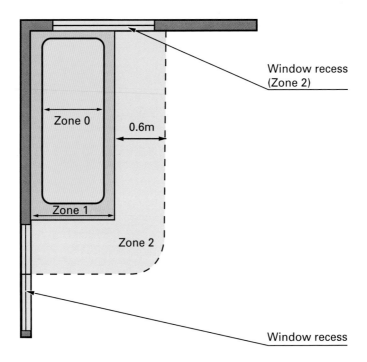

Fig 7.1 Zone dimensions. Bath tub (plan view)

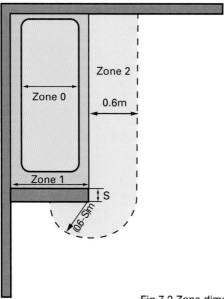

Fig 7.2 Zone dimensions. Bath tub with permanently fixed partition (plan view)

S = thickness of partition

Bath tub - elevation

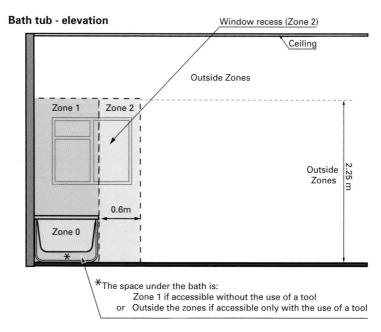

*The space under the bath is:
    Zone 1 if accessible without the use of a tool
or Outside the zones if accessible only with the use of a tool

Fig 7.3 Zone dimensions. Bath tub (elevation view)

Published by NICEIC. © Electrical Safety Council (Jan 2008)

Automatic disconnection of supply

Where the protective measure automatic disconnection of supply is used, additional protection by an RCD, with a rated residual operating current not exceeding 30 mA is required for all circuits in locations containing a bath or shower.

Careful consideration should be given to how circuits are divided to eliminate the problems with unwanted tripping of RCDs.

Supplementary bonding

Supplementary bonding has been a significant feature of the 16th edition of *BS 7671* but this has now changed with the introduction of the 17th edition.

For new installations or alterations/additions in a location containing a bath or shower, supplementary bonding will not be required if:

- the disconnection times required by Section 411 of *BS 7671* are met, *and*
- all circuits are protected by RCDs having the characteristics required by 415.1.1, *and*
- the building has protective equipotential bonding in accordance with 411.3.1.2, *and*
- all extraneous-conductive-parts of the location are effectively connected to the protective bonding. (see note below)

Note: Regulation 415.2.2 states that where doubt exists regarding the effectiveness of supplementary equipotential bonding, it shall be confirmed that the resistance R between simultaneously accessible exposed-conductive-parts and extraneous-conductive-parts fulfills the following condition:

$R \leq 50\ V / I_a$ for a.c. systems

By example, using a 30 mA RCD (required by 415.1.1.)

$R \leq 50 / 30\ mA = 1667\ \Omega$

Where supplementary bonding is required, Regulation 701.415.2 of *BS 7671* requires that the protective conductor of each circuit entering the room containing a bath or shower, be connected to the extraneous-conductive-parts by local supplementary bonding conductors complying with Regulation group 544.2.

This is carried out to prevent the occurrence of voltages between any such parts being of such magnitude as could cause danger of electric shock.

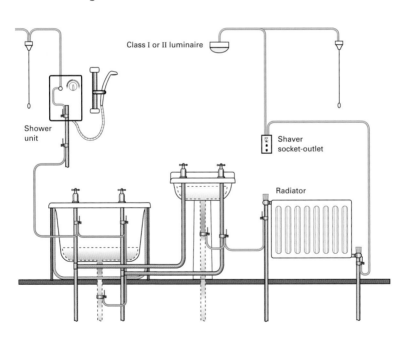

Class I or II luminaire

Shower unit

Shaver socket-outlet

Radiator

▭▭▭ Metal Pipes

▯▯▯▯ Metal waste pipes ▬▬▬ Note: Lines are not intended to represent actual routes

Fig 7.4 Supplementary equipotential bonding, typical example within a bathroom

Published by NICEIC. © Electrical Safety Council (Jan 2008)

SELV and PELV

Normally where the protection is SELV or PELV then no further devices are required for basic protection but within a room containing a bath or shower, basic protection is required in addition to the SELV or PELV by either:

i) barriers or enclosures affording degree of protection of at least IPXXB or IP2X, or
ii) insulation capable of withstanding a test voltage of 500 V a.c. for one minute.

Electrical separation

In a room containing a bath or shower the protective measure electrical separation can only be used to supply one item of current-using equipment.

A practical application of this protective measure is a shaver supply unit to *BS EN 61558-2-5*. By utilizing this measure the electrical system is completely separated from earth and from every other system. Even if the equipment provides a fault to earth, there is no shock current path.

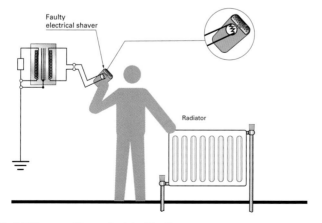

Fig 7.5 Shaver with an electrical fault

External influences

The electrical equipment installed in a room containing a bath or shower must be selected to be suitable for the conditions it is likely to experience. It must therefore be selected to ensure that the water or moisture the equipment is subjected to will not be detrimental to its safe working.

The specific requirements of IP codes relevant to each zone are shown below:

Zone 0	IPX7
Zone 1	IPX4
Zone 2	IPX4

Installation of switchgear, control gear and accessories

In zone 0:
No switchgear or accessories should be installed

In zone 1:
Only switches of SELV circuits, voltage not exceeding 12 V a.c. should be installed, the safety source being installed outside zones 0, 1 and 2. Pull cords are permitted in zone 1.

In zone 2:
Switchgear, accessories incorporating switches or socket outlets should not be installed with the exception of switches and socket-outlets of SELV circuits, (the safety source installed outside zones 0, 1 and 2) and shaver supply units to *BS EN 61558-2-5*.

Current-using equipment

The following equipment can be used in the zones indicated:

In zone 0:
* suitable for zone 0, according to the manufacturers' instructions and complies with the relevant standard, *and*
* fixed and permanently connected, *and*
* protected by SELV with a rated voltage not exceeding 12 V a.c. or 30 V d.c.

In zone 1:
Fixed and permanently connected equipment, typically:

* whirlpool units
* electric showers
* shower pumps
* equipment protected by SELV, nominal voltage not exceeding 25 V a.c. or 60 V d.c.
* ventilation equipment
* towel rails
* water heating appliances
* luminaires

Socket-outlets are now permitted in bathrooms. They should be installed no nearer than 3m from the edge of the bath or shower (measured horizontally).

As for all circuits in a bathroom they must be protected by an RCD with an $I_{\Delta n}$ not exceeding 30mA.

Fig 7.6 Electric floor heating systems

Where an electric floor heating system is to be installed, whether electric cables or thin sheet, they must meet the relevant standards and should be installed so that they have either:

* a metal sheath, *or*
* a metal enclosure, *or*
* a fine mesh metallic grid.

This must be connected to the protective conductor of the supply circuit, unless the supply circuit is SELV.

Other special locations or installations are considered outside the scope of this guide and as such reference should be made to *BS 7671* Part 7.

Appendices

Appendices

Appendix 1

Maximum earth fault loop impedance (Zs)

Automatic disconnection of supply is the most commonly used protective measure. To be effective the protective measure must provide elements for both basic and fault protection.

The protective measure automatic disconnection of supply provides:

* basic protection by basic insulation of live parts or barriers and enclosures, *and*
* fault protection by protective earthing, protective bonding and automatic disconnection in the event of a fault.

This protective measure was referred to as ADS (Automatic Disconnection of Supply)

With the ADS method of fault protection, all metalwork, including extraneous-conductive-parts and exposed-conductive-parts, in the electrical installation is connected to earth.

In the event of an earth fault, for the protective measure to work effectively, the current must be large enough to operate the protective device (fuse, circuit-breaker or RCD) disconnecting the circuit within a specified time.

Table 41.1 Maximum disconnection times

System	50 V < U_0 ≤ 120 V seconds		120 V < U_0 ≤ 230 V seconds		230 V < U_0 ≤ 400 V seconds		U_0 > 400 V seconds	
	a.c	d.c	a.c	d.c	a.c	d.c	a.c	d.c
TN	0.8	note 1	0.4	5	0.2	0.4	0.1	0.1
TT	0.3	note 1	0.2	0.4	0.07	0.2	0.04	0.1

From the above table it can be seen that for a single-phase TN installation, between 120 V and 230 V a.c. the maximum disconnection time is given as 0.4 seconds.

In a TN system where a circuit is not covered by Regulation 411.3.2.2 and Table 41.1, for example a final circuit exceeding 32 A or a distribution circuit, a disconnection time not exceeding 5 seconds is permitted. In a TT system where the same conditions apply, a disconnection time not exceeding 1 second is permitted.

Where the disconnection times prescribed on section 411.3 cannot be achieved by Regulation 411.3.2.2, 411.3.2.3 and 411.3.2.4 supplementary bonding should be installed.

Earth fault loop impedance

The earth fault loop impedance (Zs) is the impedance of the intended path of earth fault current, starting and ending at the point of the fault to earth.

In a TN system the return earth path is metallic, and is formed by the protective conductor of the supply network, either a combined protective and neutral (PEN) conductor (TN-C-S or TN-C system) or a dedicated protective conductor (TN-S system).

Published by NICEIC. © Electrical Safety Council (Jan 2008)

Appendices

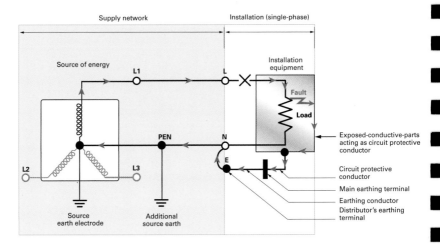

> Denotes path of fault current

X Denotes circuit-protective device (overcurrent)

Fig 8.1 TN-C-S earth fault loop (showing earth fault path)

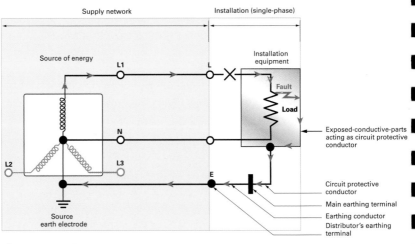

> Denotes path of fault current

X Denotes circuit-protective device (overcurrent)

Fig 8.2 TN-S earth fault loop (showing earth fault path)

Maximum value of earth fault loop impedance

The value of the earth fault loop impedance at the most remote point of each circuit must not exceed the limiting (or maximum) value permitted by the application of Regulation 411.4.5 shown below.

$$Z_S \times I_a \leq U_0$$

Where:

Z_S is the impedance in ohms (Ω) of the earth fault loop path
I_a is the current in amperes (A) causing the automatic operation of the disconnecting device within the time specified in Table 41.1 or Regulation 411.3.2.2 as appropriate.

U_0 is the nominal a.c. rms or d.c. line voltage to Earth in volts (V)

Note: Where compliance with this regulation is provided by an RCD, the disconnection times in accordance with Table 41.1 relate to prospective residual fault currents significantly higher than the rated residual operating current of the RCD (typically 2 $I_{\Delta n}$)

In the event of a fault of negligible impedance between a line conductor and an exposed-conductive-part, sufficient fault current should flow to cause the protective device to automatically disconnect the supply within the maximum time permitted by the Regulations.

This will be achieved if the maximum earth fault loop impedance for the circuit protective device is not exceeded, from tables 41.2, 41.3 and 41.4.

Appendices

Example

A shower is supplied from a final distribution board and the cable protected by a 40 A *BS EN 60898* Type B circuit-breaker. The installation is carried out in thermoplastic insulated and sheathed flat cable with protective conductor.

From Table 41.3, the maximum earth fault loop impedance (Zs) for a 40 A *BS EN 60898* circuit-breaker is 1.15Ω.

When designing the circuit a calculation would have to be carried out to check that the cable selected will meet the requirement for maximum earth fault loop impedance. It should be noted that if the earth fault loop impedance is being measured, and the conductors are not at their normal operating temperature, a note below Table 41.3 states that the measured values should be adjusted.

For the above example, if the cable was tested at 10 °C and the normal operating temperature of the thermoplastic (PVC) cable is 70 °C, then the value obtained by test would require to be divided by 0.8 and the value checked against the appropriate value from Table 41.3.

Therefore:

If the measured (tested) value was 0.5 Ω, then 0.5 ÷ 0.8 = 0.625 Ω This is less than the maximum value obtained from Table 41.3, which is 1.15Ω, therefore the circuit meets the requirements for earth fault loop impedance.

Appendix 2

Current-carrying capacities of cables

When selecting a cable for a particular application, the method of installation must be considered as described within Part 5 of this guide.

Initially, the design current of the circuit, the size and type of protective device, and the type of cable to be used must be established, where:

I_b = design circuit of the circuit (the current intended to be carried)

I_n = rated current of the protective device

Any relevant factors applicable to the installation are now applied using the formula;

$$I_t \geq \frac{I_n}{C_a \times C_g \times C_i \times C_c}$$

Where:

I_t	is the tabulated current-carrying capacity of the cable
I_n	is the rated current or current setting of the protective device
C_a	is the rating factor for ambient temperature
C_g	is the rating factor for grouping
C_i	is the derating factor for cables in thermal insulation
C_c	is the rating factor depending upon the protective device or installation condition

In addition to the above calculation, it is necessary to check that the proposed cable meets the requirements for voltage drop in accordance with Appendix 12 of *BS 7671*.

The formula for calculating voltage drop is:

$$\text{Voltage drop (in volts)} = \frac{mV \times I_b \times \text{length of cable}}{1000}$$

Appendices

Where:

mV   is the millivolts dropped per ampere per metre length taken from Tables 4D1A to 4J4A

I_b is the design current of the circuit (the current intended to be carried)

By dividing the formula by 1000 the answer is provided in volts.

BS 7671 provides two maximum voltage drop values dependant upon the type of circuit. A 3% voltage drop represents 6.9 volts and a 5% voltage drop represents 11.5 volts for 230 volt circuits.

Worked examples

Example 1

A circuit with a load of 9 kW at 230 V is to be installed with pvc flat twin and earth thermoplastic (pvc) 70 $^{\circ}$C cable. The installation method is 'clipped direct'. The circuit is to be protected by a *BS EN 60898* circuit-breaker and the length of run for the circuit is 24 m. The cable runs through an area where the ambient temperature is 35 $^{\circ}$C, and there are no other factors to be considered. The maximum voltage drop for the circuit is taken as 5%.

The design current of the circuit (I_b) is calculated

$$I_b = \frac{9000}{230} = 39.13 \text{ Amperes}$$

The protective device can now be selected where $I_n \geq I_b$, therefore the rated current of the protective device must be equal to, or greater than, the design current of the circuit.

In is selected at 40 A, as this is the next largest available

Any applicable rating factors are now applied,

$$I_t \geq \frac{I_n}{C_a \times C_g \times C_i \times C_c}$$

The only applicable rating factor is that for ambient temperature, C_a, which can be found from Table 4B1. In this example the ambient temperature is 35 $^\circ$C and the cable is pvc insulated and sheathed flat cable with protective conductor (twin and earth). This gives a factor of 0.94 from Table 4B1.

There is no factor for grouping C_g, as the cable is not grouped with other circuits. The factor for thermal insulation is not applied as the cable is not run in thermal insulation, and the factor for a protective device is not applied as the protective device is not a *BS 3036* (semi-enclosed fuse).

The calculation for the required tabulated current-carrying capacity of the cable is:

$$I_t \geq \frac{40}{0.94} = 42.55 \text{ A}$$

The value of 42.55 A is now used to select a cable from Tables 4D1A to 4J4A. The correct table used in this example is 4D5, and the correct column is one which relates to the installation method 'clipped direct' (reference method C)

From this column, the correct cable is 6 mm^2, which has a tabulated value of 47 A.

Voltage drop

A check for voltage drop must now be carried out to make sure the requirements are met.

Appendices

$$\text{Voltage drop} = \frac{\text{mV} \times I_b \times \text{length of cable}}{1000}$$

The mV/A/m value is obtained from Table 4D5 using the cable size selected (6 mm²)

mV/A/m value is therefore 7.3 mV/A/m

$$\text{Voltage drop} = \frac{7.3 \times 39.13 \times 24}{1000} = 6.86 \text{ volts}$$

A 5% voltage drop was allowed (11.5 volts), therefore the voltage drop in the example is within the maximum allowable.

A 6 mm² cable is therefore acceptable as it meets both the current-carrying capacity and voltage drop requirements.

Example 2

Cables are to be installed to supply a load of 6.5 kW at 230 V. The cables are thermosetting 90 °C singles with copper conductors and enclosed in conduit which is fixed directly to a wall for a length of 42 m. Overcurrent protection is provided by a *BS 3036* semi-enclosed fuse. The new circuit is to be run with two other similarly loaded circuits, within an ambient temperature of 30 °C. The voltage drop should be taken as 5%.

The design current (I_b) of the circuit is calculated

$$I_b = \frac{6500}{230} = 28.3 \text{ Amperes}$$

The protective device can now be selected where $I_n \geq I_b$, therefore the rated current of the BS 3036 protective device must be the next largest available.

I_n is selected as 30 A

Any applicable rating factors are now applied,

$$I_t \geq \frac{I_n}{C_a \times C_g \times C_i \times C_c}$$

The factor for C_a can be found from Table 4B1. In this example the temperature of 30 $^\circ$C and thermosetting insulation 90 $^\circ$C gives a factor of 1.00.

The factor C_g can be found from Table 4C1. As the circuit is run with two others (three in total), and is enclosed, a factor of 0.7 is applied.

The factor for C_i is not applied as the cables are not run in thermal insulation.

The factor for C_c is applied (0.725) as the protective device is a *BS 3036* semi-enclosed fuse.

The calculation for the required tabulated current-carrying capacity of the cable is:

$$I_t \geq \frac{30}{1.0 \times 0.7 \times 0.725} = 59.11 \text{ A}$$

The value of 59.11 A is now used to select a suitable cable from Tables 4D1A to 4J4A. The correct table for the cables in this example is Table 4E1A from the column relating to 'Reference method B enclosed in conduit on a wall.

From this column, the correct cable is 10 mm^2, which has a tabulated value of 75 A.

A check for voltage drop must now be carried out to make sure the requirements are met.

$$\text{Voltage drop} = \frac{\text{mV/A/m value} \times I_b \times \text{length of cable}}{1000}$$

Appendices

The mV/A/m value is obtained from Table 4E1B using the cable size selected (10 mm^2)

The mV/A/m value is from column 3 is 4.7 mV/A/m

Voltage drop = $\dfrac{4.7 \times 28.3 \times 42}{1000}$ = 5.59 volts

A 5% voltage drop was allowed (11.5 volts), therefore the voltage drop in the example is within the maximum allowable.

A 10 mm^2 cable is therefore acceptable as it meets both the current-carrying capacity and voltage drop requirements.

Published by NICEIC. © Electrical Safety Council (Jan 2008)